GCSE AQA
Core Science
Foundation Workbook

This book is for anyone doing **GCSE AQA Core Science** at foundation level.

It's full of **tricky questions**... each one designed to make you **sweat** — because that's the only way you'll get any **better**.

There are questions to see **what facts** you know. There are questions to see how well you can **apply those facts**. And there are questions to see what you know about **how science works**.

It's also got some daft bits in to try and make the whole experience at least vaguely entertaining for you.

What CGP is all about

Our sole aim here at CGP is to produce the highest quality books — carefully written, immaculately presented and dangerously close to being funny.

Then we work our socks off to get them out to you — at the cheapest possible prices.

Contents

Biology 1a — Human Biology

Biology 1b — Evolution and Environment

Chemistry 1a — Products from Rocks

Chemistry 1b — Oils, Earth and Atmosphere

Physics 1a — Energy and Electricity

Physics 1b — Radiation and the Universe

Published by Coordination Group Publications Ltd.

Editors:
Ellen Bowness, Sarah Hilton, Kate Houghton, Sharon Keeley, Kate Redmond, Ami Snelling.

Contributors:
Ben Aldiss, Antonio Angelosanto, Peter Cecil, Steve Coggins, Vikki Cunningham, Jane Davies, Philippa Falshaw, Anna-fe Guy, Paddy Gannon, Dr Iona MJ Hamilton, Rebecca Harvey, Frederick Langridge, Barbara Mascetti, Lucy Muncaster, Sidney Stringer Community School, Paul Warren, Andy Williams, Dee Wyatt.

ISBN: 978 1 84146 704 7

With thanks to Vanessa Aris, Barrie Crowther, Ian Francis and Glenn Rogers for the proofreading.
With thanks to Katie Steele for the copyright research.

Data used to construct the graph on page 24 provided by the Health Protection Agency.

Graph of sulfur dioxide emissions on page 45 compiled by NETCEN on behalf of the Department of the Environment, Food and Rural Affairs.

Graph of average surface temperature of Earth on page 46 © Crown copyright 1995, Published by the Met Office.

With thanks to the Intergovernmental Panel on Climate Change for permission to reproduce the graph of atmospheric gas concentrations used on page 46.

With thanks to East Midlands Aggregate Working Party/National Stone Centre for permission to reproduce the data used on page 60.

Groovy website: www.cgpbooks.co.uk

Printed by Elanders Hindson Ltd, Newcastle upon Tyne.
Jolly bits of clipart from CorelDRAW®

Text, design, layout and original illustrations © Coordination Group Publications Ltd. 2006
All rights reserved.

The Nervous System

Q1 Name two **sensory organs** that can detect stimuli from **distant** objects.

1. eyes ✓ 2. ears ✓

Q2 Which of the following is **not** an example of a **stimulus**? Underline your answer.

pressure chemical hearing change in body position change in temperature

can't detect it.

Q3 Draw lines to match up each **sense** with its **sense organ**, and then with the **stimulus** it detects. One has been done for you.

SENSE	ORGAN	STIMULUS
Hearing	Eye	Chemical ✓
Sight	Ear	Light ✓
Taste	Skin	Sound
Touch	Tongue	Pressure ✓

Q4 Complete the following passage by choosing the correct words from the box.

organs	motor	~~effectors~~	~~neurones~~	~~sensory~~	~~glands~~	~~electrical~~

Nerve cells or neurones ✓ transmit electrical ✓ impulses from our sense organs to the CNS. Messages from the CNS are sent to effectors ✓, which are muscles or glands ✓. The impulses are carried along motor ✓ and sensory ✓ neurones.

Q5 Some parts of the body are known as the CNS.

a) What do the letters **CNS** stand for? Central Nervous System ✓

b) Name the two main parts of the CNS.

1. Brain ✓ 2. Spinal Cord ✓

c) What type of neurone:

i) carries information **to** the CNS? Sensory neurones ✓

ii) carries instructions **from** the CNS? Motor neurones ✓

Reflexes

Think about where the impulse has to go to.

Q1 Why is a **reflex** reaction faster than a **voluntary** reaction?

They are automatic whereas voluntary the brain consciously does it.

Q2 Which of the following describes the path taken by an impulse in a **reflex** action? Underline the correct answer.

effector → sensory neurone → relay neurone → motor neurone → receptor

receptor → sensory neurone → relay neurone → motor neurone → effector

receptor → motor neurone → relay neurone → sensory neurone → effector

synapse → receptor → relay neurone → sensory neurone → effector

Q3 When you touch something hot with a finger you **automatically** pull the finger away. The diagram shows some parts of the nervous system involved in this **reflex action**.

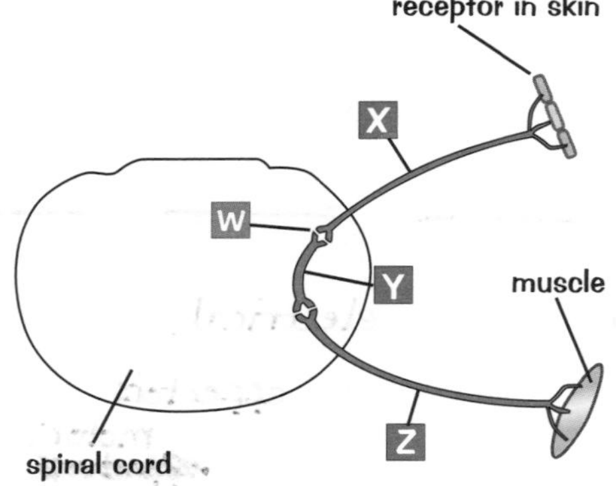

Match the following to the correct letter shown on the diagram.

W — synapse
X — motor neurone
Y — relay neurone
Z — sensory neurone

(Letters: W, X, Y, Z; Options: relay neurone, motor neurone, synapse, sensory neurone)

Q4 Give another example of a stimulus that might cause a reflex reaction. What might the response be?

stimulus: putting hand on hot fire

response: pull your hand away

Reflexes

Q5 Circle the correct answer to complete each of the following sentences.

a) Reflexes happen more **quickly** / **slowly** than considered responses.

b) The **vertebrae** / **spinal cord** can coordinate a reflex response.

c) The main purpose of a reflex is to **protect** / **display** the body.

d) Reflexes happen **with** / **without** you thinking about them.

e) The passage of information in a reflex is called a **reflex arc** / **reflex curve**.

f) A synapse is a connection between two **effectors** / **neurones**.

Q6 Look carefully at the diagrams showing two different eyes below.

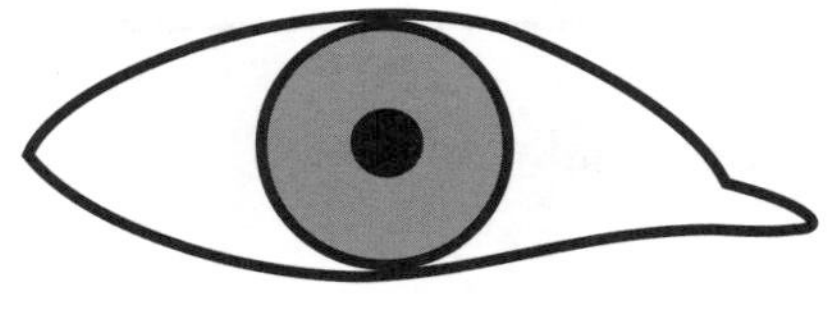

Eye A

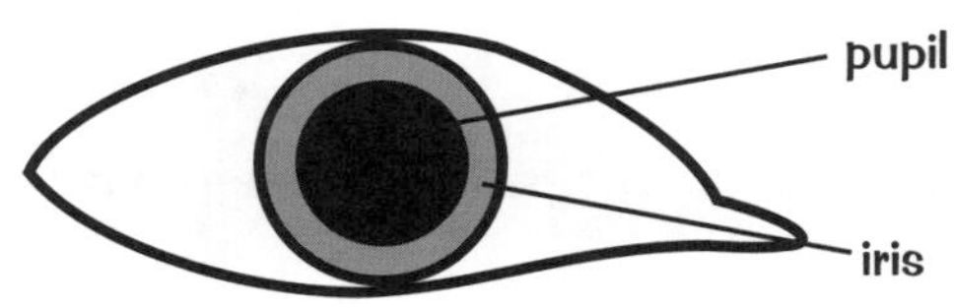

Eye B

a) Describe the difference you can see in the appearance of the two eyes.

the pupil is bigger in B.

b) Which diagram do you think shows an eye in bright light? Explain your answer.

A because the sun is bright and concerntrated light so we don't want to get to much light in.

c) Is the response illustrated by the diagrams above a considered response or a reflex response?

reflex response

d) Explain why it is an advantage to have this type of response controlling the action of the eye.

Does it automatically and you don't have to think about doing the movement

Hormones

Q1 Complete the passage using the words from below.

blood	electrical	target	chemical	glands	muscles	nerve

Hormones are .... messengers. They are produced in .... and released into the .... They are carried all around the body, but only affect certain .... cells.

Q2 Complete the table to show **where** in the body different hormones are produced.

Hormone	Where it is produced
insulin	
oestrogen	
ADH	

Q3 Give **two** differences between **nervous** responses and **hormonal** responses.

1. ....

2. ....

Q4 What is the '**fight or flight**' hormone? Why is it called this?

....

....

Q5 Fit the answers to the clues into the grid.

a) Gland that produces insulin

b) Hormone produced by the pituitary

c) Insulin controls the level of this in the blood

d) Transports hormones around the body

e) Hormone produced by the testes

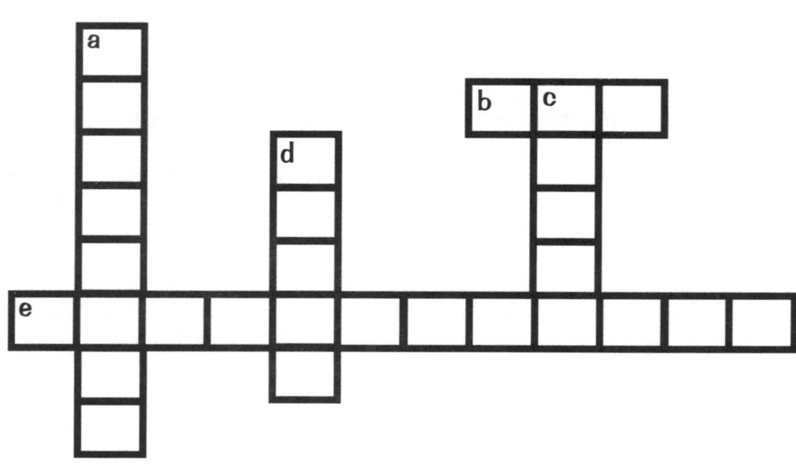

The Menstrual Cycle

Q1 Circle the correct words below to complete each sentence.

The menstrual cycle is a series of events involving the **ovaries** / **testes** and **pancreas** / **uterus**.

About once every **week** / **month** an **egg** / **ovary** is released from **an ovary** / **the uterus**.

In the uterus the **oestrogen** / **lining** is built up and then broken down.

Q2 Draw lines to match up each **stage** of the menstrual cycle with its correct **description**.

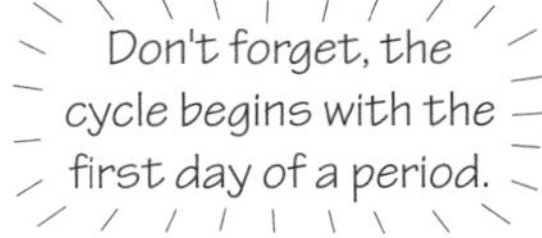

Stage 1 — The egg is released on around day 14.

Stage 2 — The start of a 'period' when the womb lining breaks down.

Stage 3 — A thick lining is maintained in the womb ready to receive a fertilised egg.

Stage 4 — An egg starts to mature in the ovary and the lining of the uterus thickens.

Q3 Complete the table to show **where** in the body each hormone is produced.

HORMONE	PRODUCED IN
FSH	
oestrogen	
LH	

Q4 FSH has two functions in the menstrual cycle.

a) What are these functions?

1. ....

2. ....

b) What effect does oestrogen have on the production of FSH?

....

Q5 Answer the following questions about **LH**.

a) What does LH stand for? ....

b) What causes LH to be released?

....

c) When does the LH cause the release of an egg from the ovary?

....

Controlling Fertility

Q1 IVF can help couples to have children.

a) What does IVF stand for? ....

b) Name two hormones that are given to women to increase the chance of an embryo implanting during IVF.

....

c) Give two problems that some women experience when undergoing IVF treatment.

....

Q2 Complete the sentences below by circling the correct words.

a) Oestrogen can be taken as a method of **fertilisation** / **contraception**.

b) Oestrogen **inhibits** / **stimulates** the production of FSH.

c) Oestrogen must be taken every **month** / **day** if it is to reduce fertility.

d) **Oestrogen** / **FSH** is present in the contraceptive pill.

Q3 Hormones can be used to **increase fertility**.

a) Name the hormone that is often given to women who are not releasing any eggs.

....

b) The passage below explains how this hormone works.
Use the words in the box to fill in the gaps. Each word should be used once.

pituitary gland **LH** **egg** **FSH** **ovary** **oestrogen**

.... stimulates the ovaries to produce .... ,

which stimulates the .... to produce ....

This stimulates the .... to release an ....

Q4 Using hormones to increase or reduce fertility in women has some **disadvantages**.
Complete the table below to show some of the disadvantages of taking hormones.

Use	Possible disadvantages
Reducing fertility	1. .... 2. ....
Increasing fertility	1. .... 2. ....

Homeostasis

Q1 a) What does the word **homeostasis** mean?

....

b) Name three things that need to be kept at the right level in the body.

1. ....

2. ....

3. ....

Q2 **Water** is **lost** from the body in different ways.

a) For each of the parts of the body listed below, explain how water is lost.

i) Skin ....

ii) Lungs ....

iii) Kidneys ....

b) The Big Brother contestants are getting on my nerves, so I put each of them on a treadmill and turn the setting to high (just to keep them quiet for a bit).

Will the contestants lose **more** or **less** water from the following body parts than they would if they sat still? Explain your answers.

i) Skin ....

....

ii) Lungs ....

....

iii) Kidneys ....

....

Q3 Ronald eats a meal that is very high in **salt**. Which of the answers below explain correctly how Ronald's body gets rid of this excess salt? Tick one or more boxes.

- [ ] Ronald's liver removes salt from his blood.
- [ ] Ronald loses salt in his sweat.
- [ ] Ronald's kidneys remove salt from his blood.
- [ ] Ronald's saliva becomes more salty, and the salt is lost when he breathes.
- [ ] Ronald gets rid of salt in his urine.

Homeostasis

Q4 The human body is usually maintained at a temperature of about 37 °C.

a) Why do humans suffer ill effects if their body temperature varies too much from this temperature?

....

....

b) Which part of your body monitors your body temperature to ensure that it is kept constant?

....

c) Suggest one method that your body can use to cool down when you're too hot.

....

Q5 The graph shows the **blood sugar levels** of a healthy person over a period of 5 hours.

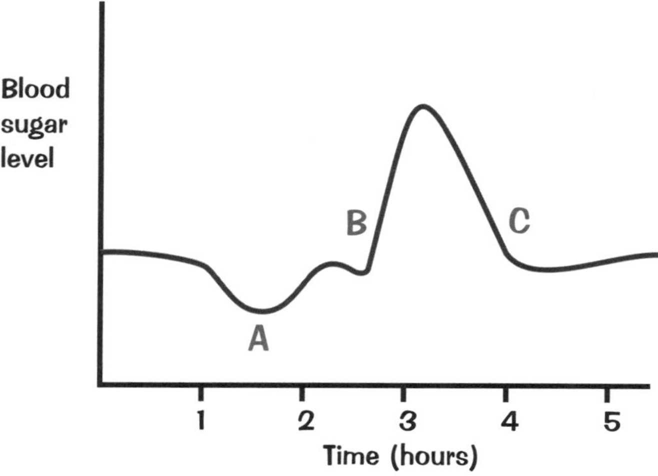

a) What might have caused the drop in blood sugar level at point A?

....

b) The blood sugar level rose quickly at point B. What could have caused this increase in sugar level?

....

c) **i)** Which hormone caused the blood sugar to return to normal at point C?

....

ii) Where in the body is this hormone produced? Underline the correct answer below.

The pituitary gland **The kidneys**

The muscles **The pancreas**

Diet and Exercise

Q1 Write '**T**' or '**F**' in each box below to show whether you think each statement is **true** or **false**.

- [ ] Proteins are our **main** energy-giving foods.
- [ ] Malnutrition and starvation are **not** the same thing.
- [ ] Deficiency diseases are due to a lack of certain nutrients.
- [ ] Fibre is **not** a necessary part of a balanced diet.
- [ ] Fats are a necessary part of a balanced diet.

Q2 Answer the following questions about **metabolism**.

a) What is meant by 'metabolic rate'?

....

....

b) What effect does being overweight have on your metabolic rate? Explain your answer.

....

....

Q3 Read each sentence below. In each case, **explain** which person you would expect to need **more energy** in their diet each day.

a) Alice works as a gardener, while Emily works in an office.

....

b) Thandi goes to the gym every day. Her friend Helen watches TV instead.

....

c) Steven weighs 8 kilograms less than his brother Michael.

....

d) Lars lives in a cold climate, while Fernando lives in a much warmer place.

....

e) Jessica and Kevin both work as dog groomers.

....

Diet and Exercise

Q4 The bar chart shows the proportions of each **food group** that make up three different foods.

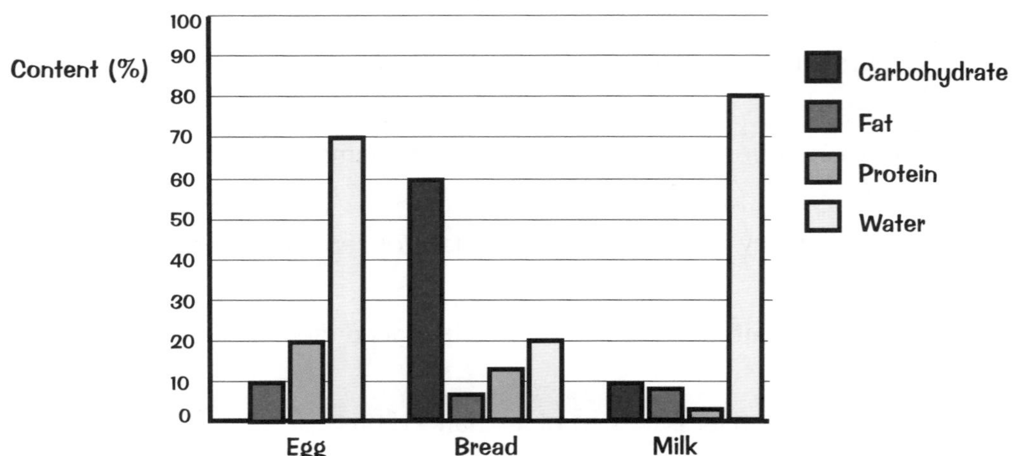

a) Which food contains the highest proportion of fat? ....

b) What is the difference between the amount of carbohydrate in 50 g of bread and the amount of carbohydrate in 50 g of milk? Give your answer in grams and show your working out.

....

....

The % in the bar chart is like the no. of grams you'd have in 100 g of the food.

c) For my lunch I have scrambled eggs on toast and a glass of milk. Suggest another food I could have to make this a more balanced meal. Explain your answer.

....

....

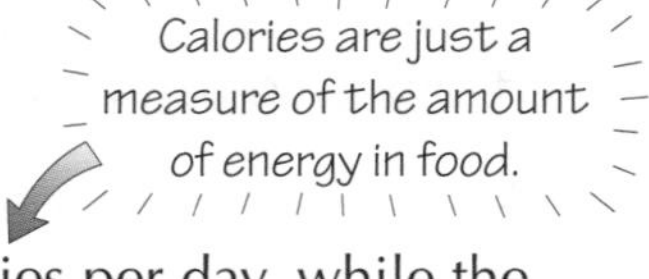

Q5 Different people need to eat **different amounts** each day.

a) It is recommended that the average woman eats 2000 Calories per day, while the average man should be eating about 2500 Calories. Explain why there is a difference.

....

....

b) Cyclists riding in the Tour de France bike race need to eat about 6000 Calories per day during the race. This is more than twice what the average man requires. Explain why.

....

....

Top Tips: Mmm, what I couldn't do with 6000 Calories per day... Anyway, the most important thing to remember is that everyone needs a balanced diet, but not everyone needs to eat exactly the same stuff. The amount you need depends on your metabolic rate and how much exercise you do.

Weight Problems

Q1 Listed below are some definitions to do with **weight problems**. Match each one with its meaning.

Obese	inability to control blood sugar levels
Arthritis	happens when not enough food is being consumed
Diabetes	lack of certain nutrients in the diet
Starvation	overweight by more than 20% of the ideal body weight
Malnutrition	inflammation of the joints that can arise due to obesity

Q2 Complete the sentences by circling the correct words.

a) Obesity can cause **high** / **low** blood pressure.

b) In developing countries too **little** / **much** food is sometimes a problem.

c) Malnutrition can cause **fatigue** / **regular periods in women**.

d) **Regular exercise** / **Hormonal problems** can lead to obesity.

Q3 **Obesity** is a serious problem in many developed countries.

a) What percentage of adults in the UK are considered to be obese? Circle the correct answer.

2% 20% 60% 80% 95%

b) Obese people are at risk from a variety of health problems.
Describe how this causes economic problems for the UK as a whole.

....

....

Q4 Lack of food is often a problem in developing countries.

a) Write down two common effects of malnutrition.

....

b) Children tend to be particularly badly affected when there is a shortage of food. Suggest why.

....

Q5 Explain why it can be difficult for researchers to collect **accurate data** on:

a) malnutrition and starvation. ....

....

....

b) obesity. ....

....

....

Cholesterol and Salt

Q1 Use the words in the box to fill in the gaps in the passage below.

blood	fatty substance	clogged	liver	diet	heart

Cholesterol is a .... that's needed for good health.
Too much cholesterol in your blood can lead to .... disease.
This is because cholesterol can be deposited in blood vessels and causes them to
become .... If your .... results in
high levels of cholesterol, your .... can remove some of it
from your ....

Q2 This question is about lipoproteins.

a) What are lipoproteins?

....

b) Name the two types of lipoprotein involved in the transport of cholesterol in the blood.

....

c) What type of lipoprotein carries cholesterol from the liver to the cells?

....

d) What does the other type of lipoprotein do?

....

....

Q3 Complete the table below showing details of the three different types of fat.

TYPE OF FAT	NUMBER OF C=C DOUBLE BONDS	EFFECT ON CHOLESTEROL IN BLOOD
Saturated		Raises the level
Polyunsaturated		
Monounsaturated	One	

Cholesterol and Salt

Q4 There are several **risk factors** for heart disease.

a) What is meant by a 'risk factor' for heart disease?

....

b) How does a high level of salt in your diet affect your body?

....

c) Give two examples of processed foods that may have a high salt content.

1. .... 2. ....

Q5 The following table shows the **fat content** of a butter substitute spread.

TYPE OF FAT	PERCENTAGE IN SPREAD
Saturated	10
Monounsaturated	35
Polyunsaturated	54
Trans fatty acids	1

a) Complete the pie chart to show this information.

Did someone mention pies?

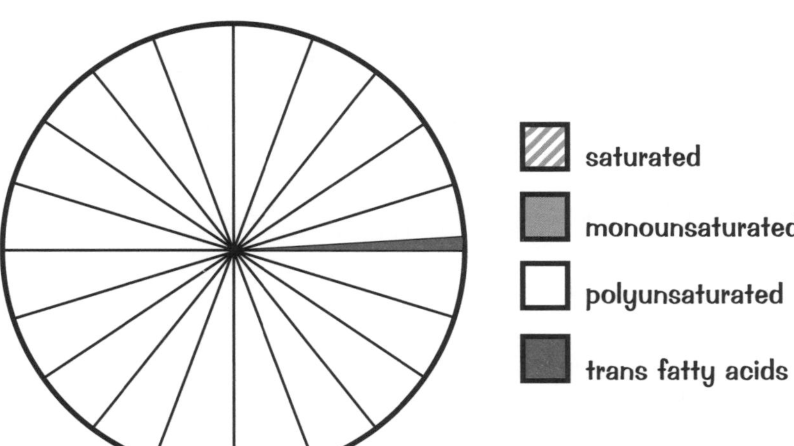

b) Suggest why this spread claims to reduce cholesterol levels.

....

....

Drugs

Q1 Drugs can change your **body chemistry**.

a) What does the term 'drug' mean?

....

b) Name two drugs that are found naturally in plants.

....

c) What does it mean if you are **addicted** to a drug?

....

....

Q2 **Thalidomide** was a drug developed in the 1950s.

a) What was thalidomide originally developed as? ....

b) Why was thalidomide given to pregnant women?

....

c) What effect does this drug have on unborn babies? ....

....

d) What is it used for now?

....

Q3 Write numbers in the boxes below to show the correct **order** in which drugs are tested.

☐ Drug is tested on human tissue.

☐ Computer models simulate a response to the drug.

☐ Human volunteers are used to test the drug.

☐ Drug is tested on live animals.

Q4 Before drugs are made freely available, clinical trials must be performed.

a) What is a 'clinical trial'?

....

b) Give two reasons why clinical trials have to be done before drugs are made freely available.

....

....

c) Explain why clinical trials can't be done on human tissue samples only.

....

....

Alcohol and Tobacco

Q1 Name three potentially **harmful** substances that can be found in tobacco smoke.

....

Q2 Draw lines to match up the following **smoking-related problems** with the correct causes.

Stroke	Damaged cilia in the windpipe can't trap microbes.
Emphysema	Smoking increases the blood pressure, which can damage the brain.
Chest infections	Air sacs in the lungs are damaged by the smoke.
Cancer	Tobacco contains a drug called nicotine.
Addiction	Cigarette smoke contains carcinogens.

Q3 a) What effect does alcohol have on the nervous system?

....

b) Give two ways that excessive alcohol consumption damages the body.

....

Q4 In the UK, the legal limit for alcohol in the blood when driving is **80 mg per 100 cm³**. The table shows the number of 'units' of alcohol in different drinks. One **unit** increases the blood alcohol level by over **20 mg per 100 cm³** in most people.

DRINK	ALCOHOL UNITS
1 pint of strong lager	3
1 pint of beer	2
1 single measure of whisky	1

a) Bill drinks two pints of strong lager. How many units of alcohol has he had? ....

b) Is Bill's blood alcohol level likely to mean that he cannot legally drive? Explain your answer.

....

....

Assume he drank the lager fairly quickly.

c) Explain why it can be dangerous to drive a car after drinking alcohol.

....

Q5 a) Why do alcohol and smoking have a bigger impact than illegal drugs in the UK?

....

b) Give two ways in which misuse of alcohol and smoking **negatively** affect the **economy** in the UK.

....

....

Investigating Drugs

Q1 Underline any of these statements about drugs that are **true**.

Cannabis is illegal in the UK.

Hard drugs are the only ones that can be addictive.

Cocaine is classed as a 'soft' drug.

Q2 A study tried to investigate the **link** between the use of **cannabis** and the use of **hard drugs**. 1000 drug users were questioned about which drugs they had used. The results are shown in the graph.

No. of people

Cannabis Hard drug

Tick the boxes next to the conclusions that can be drawn from this study.

☐ Cannabis is less dangerous than hard drugs.

☐ People are more likely to use cannabis than hard drugs.

☐ Cannabis use leads to hard drug use.

Q3 In the early 20th century the number of people developing lung cancer increased. At the same time it was noted that more people were smoking. Two possible reasons for this were proposed. **Reason 1** was that people who smoke are more likely to get lung cancer. **Reason 2** was that some genetic factor makes a person both more likely to smoke and more likely to get cancer.

a) Which of the proposed reasons has been proven to be true? ....

b) Which of the proposed reasons do you think cigarette companies favoured? Explain your answer.

....

....

Q4 Smoking is now known to be dangerous and many people try to give up. People often find this **difficult** so there are products and methods to help them. These include **hypnosis, acupuncture** and **nicotine replacement** using patches or gums.

a) Why is it hard to give up smoking?

....

b) Which of the methods listed above is supported most by scientific evidence?

....

c) Explain how nicotine gum helps someone give up smoking.

....

....

Investigating Drugs

Q5 Read the article below and answer the questions that follow.

In the UK all illegal drugs belong to one of three classes — A, B or C — depending on how harmful they are. The punishments for possessing (or dealing) class A drugs are more severe than for class C drugs.

In January 2004, cannabis was 'reclassified' as a class C drug. Previously, it had been in class B, along with amphetamines like 'speed'. The Government decided to 'downgrade' cannabis because most evidence showed that it was less harmful than the other class B drugs.

There's still a lot of debate about how harmful cannabis is, though. Many people are worried that cannabis is linked to mental illnesses like depression and schizophrenia.

In one study, scientists monitored the mental health of about 1600 teenagers at 44 different schools in Australia, over a seven-year period. They found that girls who used cannabis every day were five times more likely to suffer from depression by the age of 20. Those who used cannabis less frequently (but at least once a week) were twice as likely to suffer from depression as non-users.

Another team of scientists studied a group of older men in Sweden. Their study involved 50 000 men who did their compulsory military service between 1969 and 1970. When they began military service (aged 18–20), these men all gave details about how often they used cannabis (and other drugs). The researchers then examined the men's medical records from 1970 to 1996, to see how many of them suffered from schizophrenia in later life. They found that the more frequently a person used cannabis, the more likely they were to develop schizophrenia.

a) Write '**true**' or '**false**' next to each of the statements below.

Cannabis was legalised in 2004. ....

Punishments for dealing class A drugs are harsher than for dealing class C drugs. ....

Amphetamines are class C drugs. ....

Most evidence suggests that cannabis is more harmful than class A drugs. ....

There is still a lot of debate about how harmful cannabis is. ....

b) Some researchers studied Swedish men who had done military service between 1969 and 1970.

i) What had the men been questioned about at the beginning of their military service?

....

ii) How many years of medical records did the researchers examine?

....

iii) What did the findings suggest?

....

....

Investigating Drugs

Remember that the independent variable is the one that is changed, and the dependent variable is the one that is measured.

c) The following questions are about the **Swedish** study.

i) What were the dependent and independent variables in this study?

Dependent variable: ....

Independent variable: ....

ii) Drug use was measured by asking the men how often they used drugs. What is the main problem with this kind of '**self-reporting**'?

....

....

d) One cannabis study looked at cannabis use in teenage girls in Australian schools.

i) Complete the bar chart.

Read over the passage again if you're not sure. Remember, the bar chart gives the level for those girls that never used cannabis.

Number of girls suffering from depression after different frequencies of cannabis use

Number of girls suffering from depression

daily

at least weekly

never

Frequency of cannabis use

ii) What link is suggested by this study?

....

....

e) Fill in the information below about the **Australian** study.

Sample size: ....

Time period covered: ....

Independent variable: ....

Dependent variable: ....

Top Tips: So, after all that time, effort and money, the answer is ...erm, we dunno. Maybe it causes mental health problems, and then again, maybe it doesn't. That's science for you. There could be **another factor** that makes people more likely to take drugs **and** more likely to become mentally ill.

Health Claims

Q1 Two reports on **low-fat foods** were published on the same day.

Report A appeared in a tabloid newspaper. It said that eating the cereal 'Crunchie Bites' helps weight loss. It explained that the manufacturers of Crunchie Bites had shown that the latest girl band, Kandyfloss, had lost weight by eating it.

Report B appeared in a journal and reported that 6000 volunteers had lost weight while taking part in a clinical trial to test an experimental medicine.

a) Was the sample of each study large enough to give a valid result?

....

....

b) Do you think either of the reports is likely to be biased? Explain your answer.

....

....

c) Here is a statement from **Report A**.

> The members of Kandyfloss all ate just two bowls of Crunchie Bites each day and nothing else. Between them they lost 8 kg.

Assuming the facts in this statement are true, does it prove that eating Crunchie Bites helps you lose weight? Explain your answer.

....

....

Q2 Three **weight loss methods** appeared in the headlines last week.

1. **Hollywood star swears carrot soup aids weight loss**
2. **Survey of 10 000 dieters shows it's exercise that counts**
3. **Atkins works! 5000 in study lose weight... but what about their health?**

a) Which of these headlines are more likely to refer to **scientific studies**? Explain your answer.

....

....

b) Why might following the latest celebrity diet not always help you lose weight?

....

....

Health Claims

Q3 A drug trial involved 6000 patients with **high cholesterol levels**. 3000 patients were given drugs called **statins**, and 3000 were not.

Both groups were given advice on how to change their lifestyles to lower cholesterol.

The decrease in the patients' cholesterol levels is shown on the graph.

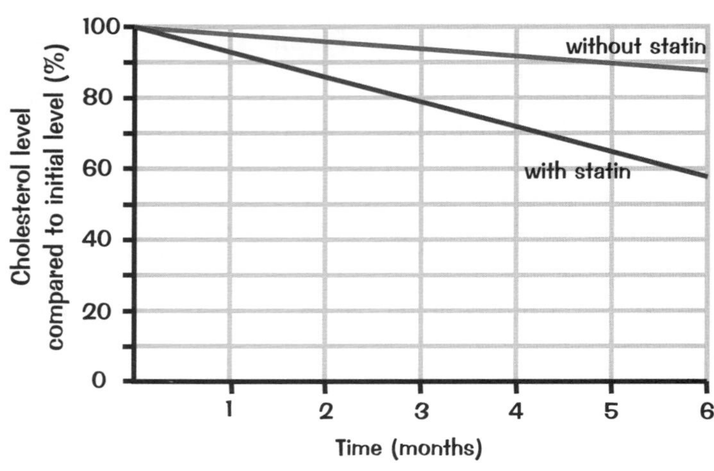

a) In which group did the cholesterol level of the participants decrease the most?

....

b) Suggest a conclusion that could be drawn from these results.

....

....

c) Which group was the **control** group?

....

Diet Pop — Each can contains less than half as many Calories as other cans of pop.

Q4 Sometimes it's hard to find out which health claims are **true**. Fill in the gaps using the words below.

vague	diet	proved	money	illegal	untrue

Advertisers want to sell a product to make .... To do this they are sometimes .... or make claims that can't be .... or are misleading. For example, they might call something '......................................', which doesn't actually tell you much about what's in it. However, it is .... to make claims that are .... and advertisers can get into trouble if they do this.

Q5 Scientists are still **not sure** whether taking cannabis leads to taking hard drugs, despite the fact that lots of studies have been carried out. Suggest why this is.

....

....

....

Fighting Disease

Q1 There are two main types of **pathogen**.

a) What is a pathogen?

....

b) Name the pathogens shown in the diagram.

A: ....

B: ....

c) Name two types of bacteria.

1. .... 2. ....

Q2 **White blood cells** protect the body from infection.

a) Give **three** ways that they do this.

....

....

....

b) Fill in the gaps using the words in the box to explain how antibodies protect the body.

antigen	antibodies	white

The .... blood cells recognise the foreign ....
They then make .... which are specific to that
.... The .... attack the foreign cell.

Q3 Put these statements in order by writing numbers in the boxes to explain one way in which the body protects itself.

☐ Platelets cause the blood to clot.

☐ The skin is damaged.

☐ A scab forms, closing the wound.

☐ Platelets in the blood are activated.

Fighting Disease

Q4 Fill in the gaps in the passage below using these words.

cells	bursts	celled	DNA	damaging	toxins	damage	copies

Bacteria are single-.................................. organisms which can multiply rapidly. Some can make you ill by .... your body cells or producing ....

Viruses are tiny particles — they are not .... They are often made up of a coat of protein and a strand of .... Viruses replicate by fooling body cells into making .... of them. The cell then .... and releases the new virus. This cell .... makes you feel ill.

Q5 Match these words to their definitions below.

pathogen	immunisation	antigen	antibody	booster

a) A substance made by white blood cells to fight infection. ....

b) An injection of inactive microbes to protect the body from future infection. ....

c) A microorganism that can cause disease. ....

d) A repeat immunisation given to top up immunity. ....

e) A protein on a pathogen which is recognised by the immune system. ....

Q6 If a person has an organ transplant, they may have to take drugs to **suppress** their immune system and stop the organ being **rejected**. Why is it important that these people **avoid infection**?

....

....

Top Tips: Pathogens are all nasty little blighters that can make you ill if they manage to get inside you. Bacteria and viruses have totally different structures and methods of attack — make sure you know the differences. And remember — antibiotics kill bacteria, not viruses.

Fighting Disease

Q7 Circle the correct words in the passage below to explain how **immunisation** works.

When a person is **defended / infected** by a pathogen, their white blood cells take time to learn how to fight it. During that time the person can get ill. To avoid this people can be **immunised / given painkillers**. This involves injecting dead or **active / inactive** pathogens. These still carry the same **antigens / antibodies** as the live pathogens and so the white blood cells learn to make the right **antigens / antibodies**. They can then fight **all pathogens / the same pathogen** much more quickly in future.

Q8 These sentences explain how bacteria become **resistant** to antibiotics. Put them in the right order.

- [ ] Sanjay feels better so he **doesn't** finish the full course of antibiotics.
- [ ] **Most** of the bacteria causing his infection are killed by the antibiotics.
- [ ] These bacteria reproduce to give a **resistant strain**.
- [ ] Some of the bacteria were **more resistant** to the antibiotics and are still alive.
- [ ] Sanjay is given **antibiotics** for an infection.

Q9 A new medicine called 'Killcold' contains **painkillers** and **decongestants**.

a) Explain why its name isn't strictly accurate.

....

....

b) Why don't doctors give antibiotics for colds?

....

....

c) Why is it more difficult to develop drugs to destroy viruses than it is to develop drugs to kill bacteria?

....

....

Think about where in the body viruses like to hang out so that they can replicate themselves.

Treating Disease — Past and Future

Q1 Ignaz Semmelweiss worked in a hospital in Vienna in the 1840s. The graph shows the percentage of women dying after childbirth, before and after a **change** that he made.

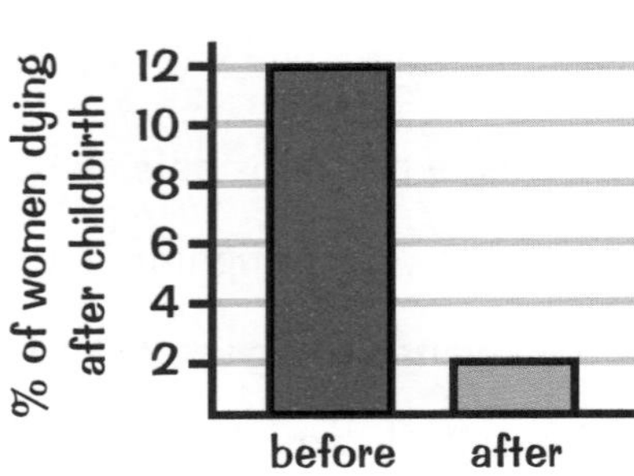

a) How did the change affect the number of women dying?

....

b) The change he made was telling doctors to wash their hands in antiseptic solution when entering a ward. Why did this have an effect?

....

....

Q2 The graph shows the number of people **catching** measles and being **vaccinated** against it in recent years in the UK.

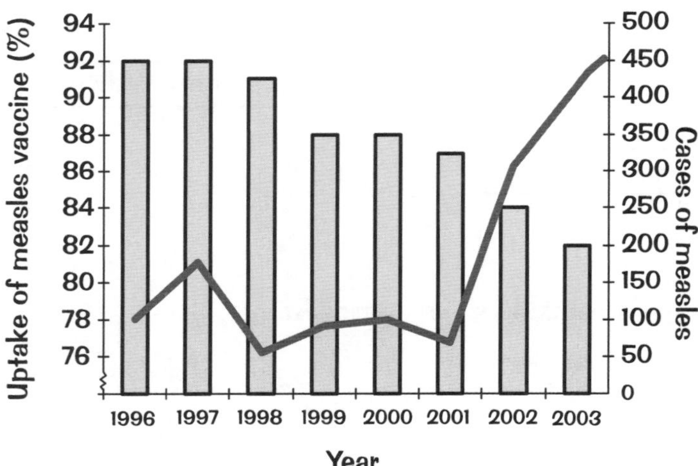

a) Complete the table of results below.

	1996	2003
uptake of vaccine		
no. of measles cases		

b) What conclusion could be drawn from this table of results?

....

....

Treating Disease — Past and Future

Q3 Bacteria and viruses can evolve to be **resistant** to medicines.

a) Name a strain of bacteria that is resistant to certain antibiotics.

....

b) Why is resistance a problem?

....

....

c) Give an example of a virus that evolves quickly. ....

Q4 Answer the questions below about **immunisation**.

a) Explain how immunisations have changed the pattern of disease in the UK.

....

....

b) Name a disease that has been **eradicated** worldwide because of immunisation programmes.

....

c) Describe **two** problems that occasionally occur with vaccines.

....

....

Q5 The MMR vaccine protects against measles, mumps and rubella. There is a small risk that children will suffer serious side effects to the vaccine such as meningitis or convulsions. However, the Government recommends that **all** children are given the MMR vaccine. Explain why this is.

....

....

....

Top Tips:

Of course, Darwin was right when he said that evolution happens gradually over many generations. The trouble is, with bacteria and viruses, a whole generation can take about ten minutes. Hmmm.

Mixed Questions — Biology 1a

Q1 The diagram shows a runner waiting to start a race in the Olympic Games.

a) Give one sense organ that the athlete is relying on at the start of this race, and state the type of receptors it uses.

....

b) When the athlete starts the race, information will travel around his body via neurones.

i) What is the difference between motor neurones and sensory neurones?

....

....

ii) Explain how a nerve signal passes from one neurone to the next.

....

....

c) Some information is sent around the body using hormones rather than nervous impulses.

i) How do hormones travel around the body?

....

ii) Describe **three** differences in the way nerves and hormones work in the body.

....

....

....

Q2 The lining of a woman's uterus changes in thickness in a **monthly cycle**.

a) What is this monthly cycle called? ....

b) The diagram on the right shows these changes in thickness during a 28-day cycle.

When is the lining of the uterus thickest?

Between day .... and day ....

c) Circle the correct name for the monthly loss of blood: **ovulation** **menstruation** **mitosis**

d) Explain how the oestrogen in the contraceptive pill prevents pregnancy.

....

....

Mixed Questions — Biology 1a

Q3 A **balanced diet** is very important in staying healthy.

a) Underline the type of lipoprotein that's known as "good cholesterol". **HDL** **LDL**

b) Which types of fat should you **avoid eating** if you are trying to improve your LDL/HDL balance?

....

c) Obesity is a major problem in some developed countries. What are the most common causes?

....

d) Name a major health problem associated with a diet high in fats and salt.

....

Q4 a) Circle the best word or phrase from each pair to complete the sentences below.

i) **Carbohydrates** / **Vitamins** are needed in tiny amounts to keep you healthy.

ii) Malnutrition tends to be a problem in **developed** / **developing** countries.

iii) An overweight person usually has a **higher** / **lower** metabolic rate than an average person.

iv) A farmer is likely to need a lot **more** / **less** energy than someone working in a call centre.

v) Carbohydrates are broken down into sugars to provide **energy** / **materials** to build new cells.

b) Water is a vital part of our diet and the body's water level is controlled by **homeostasis**.

i) Name **three** ways that water is lost from the body.

....

....

....

ii) What happens to the **amount** of urine that people produce if the air temperature is high?

....

Q5 Scientists spend a lot of time **researching** new diets and drugs.

a) Why are drugs tested on animals before they are used in clinical trials?

....

b) List **three** factors that can give you an indication of how reliable a scientific report is.

....

....

....

Mixed Questions — Biology 1a

Q6 Tick the boxes below that are next to **true** statements.

It is now widely accepted that smoking increases the risk of lung cancer. ☐

Alcohol doesn't tend to cause serious problems because it is legal. ☐

It is now widely accepted that using cannabis increases the risk of mental health problems. ☐

Until more scientific evidence is available, scientists can't be sure that smoking is harmful. ☐

Some studies have found a link between cannabis use and mental health problems. ☐

It has been proven that the desire to take cannabis and other drugs is genetic. ☐

Q7 Gavin and Van carried out an experiment at school to investigate the effectiveness of six different **antibiotics** (1–6). They spread some bacteria onto a sterile agar plate. They then placed discs of filter paper, impregnated with the six different antibiotics, onto the bacterial culture.

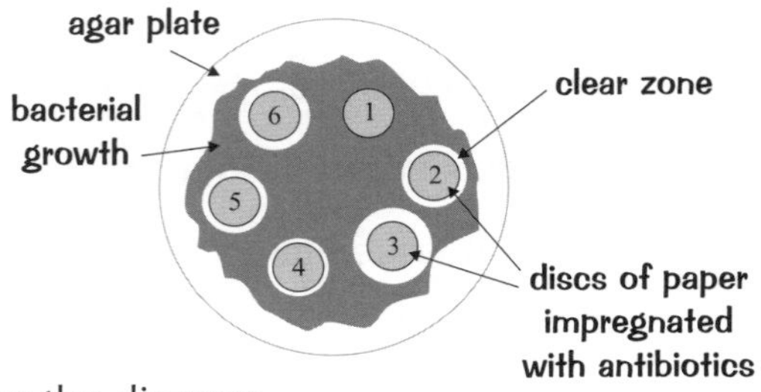

a) Explain what has happened in the "clear zone" labelled on the diagram.

....

b) Which of the antibiotics (1–6) was the most effective against these bacteria? ....

c) Would these antibiotics also work against the flu? Explain your answer.

Flu is caused by viruses.

....

....

d) Why do doctors prescribe antibiotics as infrequently as possible?

....

....

e) The body has its own ways of dealing with pathogens. Explain how some white blood cells use **antibodies** to kill bacteria.

....

....

f) Why are people vaccinated against diseases such as mumps even though their white blood cells are able to fight the pathogens?

....

Adapt and Survive

Q1 Organisms living in different conditions face different challenges.

a) Why would many animals find it difficult to survive in:

i) a desert ....

....

ii) the Arctic ....

....

b) Why would many plants find it difficult to survive living:

i) on a forest floor ....

....

ii) in the desert ....

....

Q2 The picture shows a camel, which lives in the **desert**.
Suggest the benefit to the camel of having the following features:

a) wide feet ....

....

b) two small, fatty humps ....

....

c) long eyelashes ....

....

Q3 The picture shows a **ladybird**.

a) Describe one feature the ladybird has that helps it ward off predators.

....

b) State two other features that animals use to protect themselves from predators.
Name an animal that has each of these features.

1. Feature: .... **Animal:** ....

2. Feature: .... **Animal:** ....

Adapt and Survive

Q4 Pictures of a **polar bear** and a small rodent called a **kangaroo rat** are shown below.

Diagrams are not to scale.

a) Which of these animals do you think has the smallest body surface area? ....

b) Which animal has the smallest body surface area **compared to its volume**? ....

This is a tricky one. Remember, long, thin shapes have a big surface area compared to their volume.

c) Explain how this animal's **shape** helps to reduce its body surface area compared to its volume.

....

d) Does having a **smaller** body surface area compared to volume mean that more or less **heat** can be lost from an animal's body?

....

e) The kangaroo rat lives in hot desert regions. Would you expect its body surface area compared to volume to be bigger or smaller than the polar bear's? Explain why.

....

....

....

Q5 The picture shows a **cactus** plant.

a) Where are cactus plants usually found? Underline the correct answer below.

In Arctic regions **In the desert** **In the mountains** **Near the sea**

b) Explain how each of the following parts of the cactus help it to survive in its normal habitat.

i) Spines ....

....

ii) Stem ....

....

iii) Roots ....

....

Populations and Competition

Q1 Population sizes depend on a number of factors.

a) Define the term '**population**'.

....

....

b) State three factors that can affect the size of a population.

1. .... **2.** .... **3.** ....

Q2 State whether the populations **in bold** below will **increase** or **decrease**.

a) A drought dries up a pond where **frogs** spawn. ....

b) The size of a herd of deer living near a **wolf** pack increases. ....

c) A disease kills most of the trees in which **cuckoos** nest. ....

d) A pesticide kills most of the insects that feed on a field of **cabbages**. ....

Q3 Indicate whether each of the following shows animals trying to compete (**C**) or acting as predators (**P**) by putting a cross in the correct column.

BEHAVIOUR	C	P
Stags grow antlers during the mating season		
A pack of wolves work together to kill a moose		
A magpie chases a sparrow away from a bird-table		
Spiders spin webs to trap flies		
Lions chase leopards and cheetahs from their territory		

Q4 **Algae** are tiny plants that are eaten by **fish**. The graph shows how the size of a population of algae in a pond varied throughout one year.

a) Suggest two conditions that may have changed in the pond to give more algae in April than in January.

....

b) The number of **fish** in the pond increased rapidly during one month of the year. Suggest which month this was. Explain your answer.

....

....

Variation in Plants and Animals

Q1 The table below gives the heights of pupils in Year 7 at a school to the nearest cm.

HEIGHT RANGE (cm)	NO. OF PUPILS
135–139	2
140–144	16
145–149	26
150–154	15
155–159	4
160–164	1

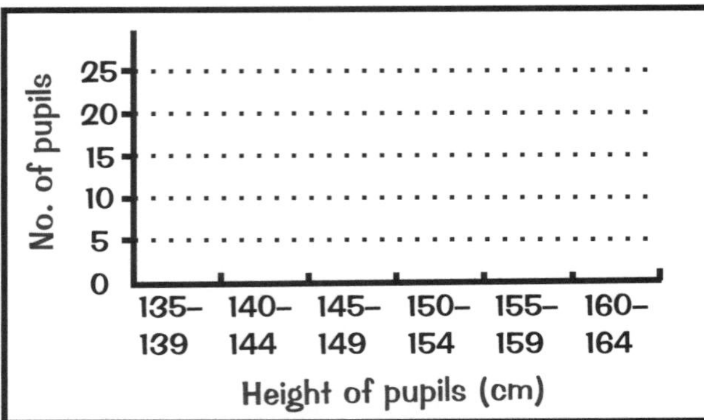

a) Plot a bar chart for the results on the grid provided.

b) Within which of the height ranges are the most students found? ....

c) The tallest pupil is 164 cm, and the shortest is 135.5 cm.
What is the height **range** seen in this year group? ....

d) Underline the reason for the variation in the children's height.

genes only environment only both genes and environment

Q2 Tick the boxes to indicate whether each of these statements is **true** or **false**.

		True	False
a)	If your parents are overweight then it is unlikely you will be slim, regardless of diet.	☐	☐
b)	When you dye your hair you alter the genes that determine your hair colour.	☐	☐
c)	If both of your parents are tall then it is likely that you will be tall.	☐	☐
d)	You can only learn to ride a bike if your parents learned to cycle.	☐	☐

Q3 Read each of the statements below about Daniel. In each case, decide whether the situation described is **mostly due to genes** (write '**G**') or to **environment** (write '**E**').

a) Daniel's hair is quite short and spikey. ....

b) His hair grows really fast. ....

c) When Daniel was born he had no hair at all. ....

d) When Daniel first went to school he found he was naturally good at maths. ....

e) He had to try hard to catch up in history, but now he's near the top of the class. ....

f) When Daniel started school he could already read, because his mum had taught him. ....

Top Tips: Don't get the wrong idea about this environment stuff — it isn't about recycling or saving the whales. The environment we're talking about here covers everything around you.

Variation in Plants and Animals

Q4 Complete this passage by circling the **best** word or phrase from each highlighted pair.

> Usually, organisms of the same species **have differences / are identical**. This is partly because different organisms have different **genes / cells**, which they inherit from their parents. **Reptiles / Identical twins** are exceptions to this. But even these usually have some different features, such as **hair style / eye colour**, and that is due to their **diet / environment**. The differences between individual organisms are known as **variation / inheritance**.

Q5 Helen and Stephanie are identical twins.

a) Do you think that the picture shows both Helen and Stephanie's natural hair colour? Explain your answer.

....

....

b) Helen weighs 7 kg more than Stephanie. Say whether this is due to genes, environment or both, and explain your answer.

....

....

c) Stephanie has a birthmark shaped like Wayne Rooney on her left shoulder. Helen doesn't. Do you think birthmarks are caused by genes? Explain why.

....

....

Genes, Chromosomes and DNA

Q1 Draw lines to match up the following terms with their definitions.

a)	DNA	different forms of a gene
b)	Gene	the chemical that genetic material is made from
c)	Alleles	part of a chromosome that controls a characteristic

Q2 Ben labelled some sketches of genetic material but he made some mistakes. Under each diagram, write down what the correct label should be.

a)

....

b)

....

c)

....

Q3 Write '**true**' or '**false**' next to each of the statements about chromosomes below.

a) Each chromosome is responsible for one characteristic, e.g. eye colour. ....

b) All the chromosomes in the nucleus of one cell come from the same parent. ....

c) The chromosomes in human cells pair up to give 46 pairs of chromosomes. ....

Q4 Complete the passage using some of the words given below.

DNA	nucleus	genes	chromosomes	membrane	allele

Each cell of the body contains a structure called the ....

This structure contains strands of genetic information, packaged into ....

These strands are made of a chemical called ....

Sections of genetic material that control different characteristics are called ....

Q5 Write out these structures in order of size, **starting with the smallest**.

nucleus	gene	chromosome	cell

1. .... 2. .... 3. .... 4. ....

Reproduction

Q1 There are **two types** of reproduction.

a) Name each type. .... and ....

b) Name the type of reproduction that produces new individuals in mammals. ....

Q2 Put crosses in the correct columns to identify the features of each type of reproduction.

FEATURE	SEXUAL	ASEXUAL
There is only one parent		
Offspring has a different genetic make-up to the parent		
Offspring are called clones		
Gametes are produced in this type of reproduction		

Billy...?

Q3 In **sexual** reproduction, how many **chromosomes** are there in the following human cells?

a) Egg cell ....

b) Body cell ....

c) Sperm cell ....

d) Fertilised egg cell ....

Q4 Circle the correct words in each statement below to complete the sentences.

a) Sexual reproduction involves **one** / **two** individual(s).

b) The cells that are involved in asexual reproduction are called **parent cells** / **gametes**.

c) Asexual reproduction produces offspring with **identical** / **different** genes to the parent.

d) In sexual reproduction the sperm cell contains **the same number of** / **half as many** chromosomes as the **fertilised** egg.

e) **Asexual** / **Sexual** reproduction creates offspring with different characteristics to the parent(s).

Q5 Using the definitions on the right-hand side to help, unscramble each of these words.

a) **sleocn** (offspring that are identical to their parent) ....

b) **msepr** (the male gamete) ....

c) **itlisteanriof** (the process that occurs when two gametes fuse) ....

Cloning

Q1 Draw lines to match each type of **cloning** to its description.

adult cell cloning	many plants are created from a few cells
tissue culture	many animals are created from a split embryo
cuttings	genetic material is inserted into an 'empty' egg cell
embryo transplants	identical plants are created from parts of a parent plant

Q2 Use words from below to fill in the blanks in the passage about **tissue culture**.

growth	slowly	clones	space	quickly	leaves	cells	sperm	hormones

A few .... from a good parent plant are placed in a .... medium containing .... These grow into new plants which are .... of the parent plant. Tissue culture allows you to grow new plants very .... and it requires very little ....

Q3 Below are statements about the **different types** of cloning. Write down the type of cloning that each statement is referring to — **adult cell cloning**, **embryo transplants**, **cuttings** or **tissue culture**.

a) The new organisms produced are **not** clones of the parent organisms.

....

b) A particularly good plant can be reproduced quickly and cheaply by most gardeners.

....

c) This technique was famously used to produce a cloned sheep called Dolly.

....

d) This technique could be used to produce embryos that are clones of people with diseases, in order to use tissues or organs grown from the embryonic stem cells to replace faulty ones.

....

e) Cells from a parent are placed in a growth medium where they develop into new individuals.

....

Cloning

Q4 Joe has a herd of cows and he wants them all to have calves, but **only** wants to breed from his champion bull and prize cow.

a) Name a method Joe could use to achieve this. ....

b) Put the steps involved in this process **in order** by writing numbers in the boxes.

☐ An egg cell is fertilised by a sperm cell in a laboratory.

☐ The embryos grow into baby calves.

☐ Each cloned embryo is implanted into a different cow.

☐ An embryo develops and is split many times to form clones.

☐ Sperm cells are taken from the champion bull and egg cells are taken from the prize cow.

c) Which of the animals involved in this process will be genetically identical?

....

d) Explain one disadvantage of this method.

....

....

Q5 **Adult cell cloning** was used to create **Dolly the sheep**.

a) Describe the process of adult cell cloning.

....

....

....

b) Explain how this process could be adapted and used to treat problems such as kidney disease.

....

....

....

Top Tips: Cloning isn't just going on in silly sci-fi films — a lot of scientific research is being done into how it can be used to help people.

Genetic Engineering

Q1 State the meaning of the term '**genetic engineering**'.

....

....

Q2 Circle the correct words below to explain **how** genetic engineering is carried out.

The useful **gene / nucleus** is 'cut' from the donor organism's chromosome using **a scalpel / enzymes**. The same **scalpel / enzymes** are then used to cut the host organism's chromosome and the useful **gene / enzyme** is inserted. This technique is known as gene **transplantation / splicing**.

Q3 Complete the passage below using the words given.

genes	disease	engineering	fertilisation	milk	changing

Scientists have developed a way to place useful .... into plants and animals soon after .... This means these organisms develop new features. Animals that produce drugs in their .... have been created, as well as plants which produce better yields and are .... resistant. Adding, removing or .... genes is called genetic ....

Q4 Billy has **cystic fibrosis**. Say briefly how genetic engineering could be used to help him.

....

....

Q5 Some people are **worried** about genetic engineering.

a) Explain why some people are concerned about genetic engineering.

....

....

b) Do you think that scientists should be carrying out genetic engineering? Explain your answer.

....

....

....

Genetic Engineering

Q6 Read the article below about **GM crops** and answer the questions that follow.

There are many reasons for genetically modifying crops. Two important reasons are to make them pest-resistant and to make them resistant to herbicides (weedkillers).

At the moment no one's growing any GM crops in the UK. Recently, though, some farmers took part in crop trials set up by the Government, to see what effects growing herbicide-tolerant GM crops might have on wildlife. There were four kinds of crops in the trials — beet, spring oilseed rape, maize and winter oilseed rape.

Fields of various sizes were chosen for the study. In each case, the farmer split one of their normal fields in half. They then grew a 'normal' crop in one half and its GM equivalent in the other. Apart from that, they did everything normally — ploughing the field, adding fertiliser etc. in the same way as they usually would. The only difference was with herbicides — with the GM crops, the farmers followed instructions about how much of which herbicides to use, and when to apply them. They applied herbicides to the 'normal' crop as they usually would.

As the crops grew, the government researchers counted the number of weeds growing, and the number of weed seeds produced in each half of the field. They also monitored the populations of insects, slugs, spiders and other wildlife.

The researchers found that with three crops (beet, spring oilseed rape and winter oilseed rape), growing normal crops was better for wildlife — they found more butterflies and bees on the normal crops. They also found more flowering weeds (the kinds that butterflies and bees prefer) on the side with normal crops. With maize, oddly, the opposite seemed to be true — there were more weeds, and more butterflies and bees, around the GM crops.

a) Crops are **genetically modified** for various reasons.

i) State the two reasons given in the article for genetically modifying crops.

....

....

ii) Write down one other possible reason for genetically modifying crops.

....

b) Explain the **purpose** of the trial described in the article.

....

....

....

Farmer Gideon had a brand new combine harvester and he wasn't going to give anyone the keys.

Genetic Engineering

c) For each type of crop, a 'normal' version and a GM equivalent was used.

i) Were the normal or the GM crops generally found to be better for wildlife? Circle your answer.

Normal crops **GM crops**

ii) What made this type of crop more attractive to organisms like bees and butterflies?

....

....

iii) Which type of crop gave an unexpected result at the end of this trial?

....

d) Herbicides were used on **both** the normal and the GM crops in this trial.

Think about the amount of herbicide that can be used.

i) Explain why fewer weeds normally grow among herbicide-resistant crops.

....

....

ii) Explain how growing herbicide-resistant crops in the UK could benefit:

farmers. ....

....

shoppers buying these products. ....

....

e) Some people **don't** want GM crops grown in the UK.

i) Some people don't want GM crops to be grown because they think it will reduce the amount of wildlife living on farmland. Do you think that this trial supports this concern? Explain your answer.

....

....

ii) Give two reasons, other than the effect on wildlife and biodiversity, why people are concerned about GM crops being widely grown in the UK.

....

....

....

Evolution

Q1 Traces of animals which lived millions of years ago are sometimes found in pieces of rock.

a) What do we call these traces? ....

b) Fill in the gaps in the paragraph below to explain how these traces form. Use the words in the box. Each word may be used more than once or not at all.

evolution	fossils	shells	minerals	roots	tissues	skeletons

.... form in rocks as .... replace slowly decaying .... Features that commonly form .... include .... and ....

Q2 Fossils were found in this sample of rock.

Fossil A

Fossil B

a) Which fossil do you think is the oldest? ....

b) The two fossils look very similar. Scientists think that the species of animal that formed the older fossil gradually changed into the species that formed the more recent fossil. What is this process of change called?

....

Q3 No one really knows how life began. There are several **ideas**, for example:

Idea 1 — **Life started in a primordial swamp.**

Idea 2 — **God created life.**

Idea 3 — **Comets carried the molecules needed for life to begin to Earth.**

Remember, life has been around a long time now...

a) Which of these do you think are scientific ideas? ....

b) Why is it difficult for scientists to find evidence to support a particular theory of the origin of life?

....

Q4 a) Roughly how many species have been identified on Earth? Circle one number below.

1500 **15 000** **150 000** **1 500 000**

b) There are actually many more species than this. Some scientists think there might be as many as 100 million species on Earth. Suggest why this figure is so much bigger than the figure in part a).

....

....

Q5 a) Dinosaurs, mammoths and dodos are all animals that are now 'extinct'. What does this mean?

....

b) How do we know about extinct animals? ....

....

Evolution

Q6 Several **theories** have been suggested to explain how **new species** arise over time. Match each theory with the person or group who suggested it. Choose from:

The Church	Darwin	Lamarck

a) New features arise randomly. If these are beneficial, they will be passed on to offspring and eventually a new species results. ....

b) God created new species. (Tricky one, this.) ....

c) A feature which an organism uses a lot will become more developed and this change will be passed on to offspring. Eventually a new species results. ....

Q7 Charles Darwin first came up with the theory of **natural selection** in the 1830s. Fill in the gaps in the paragraph below to explain his theory.

Some individuals are well .... to their environment. These individuals are more likely to .... and pass on beneficial .... to their offspring. Other individuals are not well .... to their environment. These are more likely to .... before they can breed.

Q8 Warfarin was once widely used as a **poison** to kill rats in the UK. Over time, however, some rats developed an **immunity** to warfarin and this immunity then spread quickly through the rat population.

a) If the gene for immunity to warfarin was not found in the rat population originally, how did it first appear?

....

b) Explain why the immunity to warfarin spread quickly through the rat population.

....

....

....

Evolution

Q9 Some mammals were exposed to a chemical which damaged the **DNA** in their **skin cells**. These mammals developed skin cancer. They then had offspring, **none** of which developed skin cancer.

a) What do we call a change in DNA?

....

b) Why was the skin cancer not passed on to the offspring?

....

....

c) Some of the offspring had new mutations in the DNA in each of their cells.
These had not been present in all the cells of their parents.
These mutations were also thought to be due to the chemical. Which cells in the bodies of the parent animals do you think had been damaged, other than the skin cells?

....

Q10 Giraffes used to have much **shorter** necks than they do today.

a) The statements below explain Darwin's theory about how their neck length changed. Write numbers in the boxes to show the **order** the statements should be in.

- [ ] The giraffes competed for food from low branches. This food started to become scarce. Many giraffes died before they could breed.
- [ ] More long-necked giraffes survived to breed, so more giraffes were born with long necks.
- [ ] A giraffe was born with a longer neck than normal. The long-necked giraffe was able to eat more food.
- [ ] The long-necked giraffe survived to have lots of offspring that all had longer necks.
- [1] All giraffes had short necks.
- [6] All giraffes had long necks.

b) Lamarck's theory of how giraffes evolved to have long necks was different from Darwin's. How would Lamarck have explained this evolution?

Think about short giraffes trying to stretch up to reach the food that was left on the high branches.

....

....

....

Top Tips: Lamarck might not have got it right, but it was a bright idea, seeing as he didn't know about DNA. But you do, so no excuses. You've got to feel a bit sorry for those poor short-necked giraffes going hungry while the long-necked giraffes scoffed loads of food.

Human Impact on the Environment

Q1 Look at the graph below and answer the questions that follow.

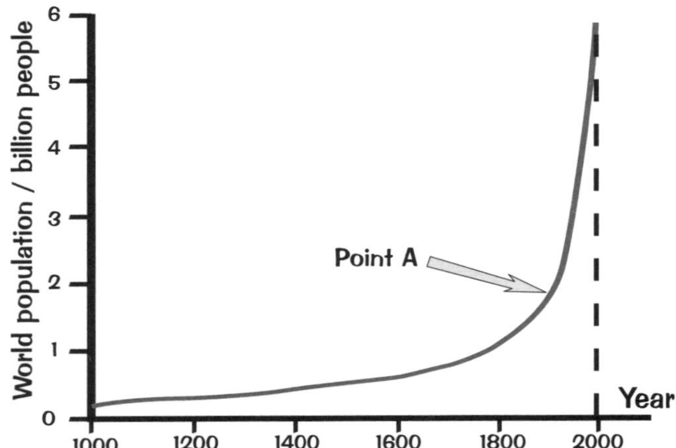

a) Which of these are valid conclusions based on this graph? Tick one or more boxes.

- [ ] There are about 6 billion people in the world today.
- [ ] There are too many people in the world.
- [ ] The human population will continue to grow at an extremely fast rate.
- [ ] The human population has been increasing rapidly for about 200 years.

Hint: think about what you'd know for sure if you only had this graph to go on.

b) Suggest a reason for the increase after point A.

....

Q2 Humans are having an **increasing impact** on their environment. One reason for this is that the world **population** is growing.

a) Suggest another reason for the increasing impact.

....

b) Modern people are using more of the Earth's natural resources than previous generations did. Suggest two things that modern people are using more of.

1. .... 2. ....

c) What is the problem with using more of these things?

....

....

Human Impact on the Environment

Q3 The growing human population is producing more **waste** which can pollute water, land and air.

a) Give **two** ways that each of the following can be polluted by human activities.

i) Water: ....

....

ii) Land: ....

....

iii) Air: ....

....

b) Other than dumping waste, name two human activities that reduce the amount of land available for other animals.

1. .... 2. ....

Q4 Circle the correct word to complete each sentence below.

a) The size of the human population now is **bigger** / **smaller** than it was 1000 years ago.

b) The growth of the human population now is **slower** / **faster** than it was 1000 years ago.

c) The human impact on the environment now is **less** / **greater** than it was 1000 years ago.

Q5 The graph below shows the amount of sulfur dioxide released in the UK between 1970 and 2003.

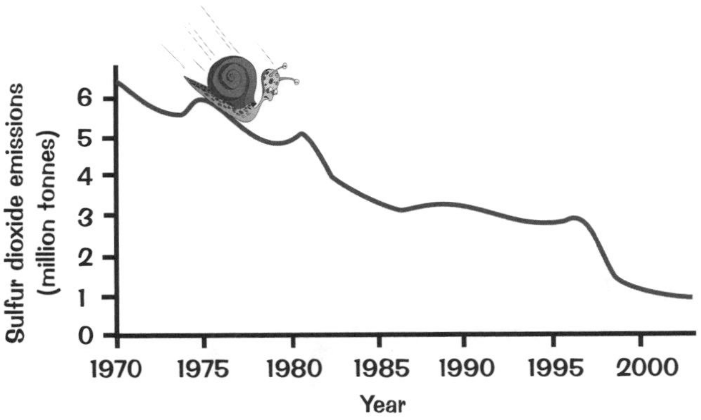

a) In which year shown on the graph were sulfur dioxide emissions highest? ....

b) Approximately how much sulfur dioxide was emitted in 2003? ....

c) Name one problem caused by sulfur dioxide.

....

The Greenhouse Effect

Q1 The greenhouse effect keeps the Earth warm.

a) Circle the correct words in the passage below.

> The Earth receives energy from the **Sun / Moon**. Some of this energy is **conducted / radiated** back out into space and some is absorbed by **rain / certain gases** in the atmosphere. This trapped energy **warms / cools** the atmosphere. The gases are known as **CFCs / greenhouse gases**. They act as a giant **insulating blanket / microwave**.

b) What would happen if there were no greenhouse gases?

....

....

c) In recent years the amounts of greenhouse gases in the atmosphere have increased. What effect is this likely to have had on the temperature of the Earth?

....

Q2 The graph shows changes in the **average surface temperature** since 1859.

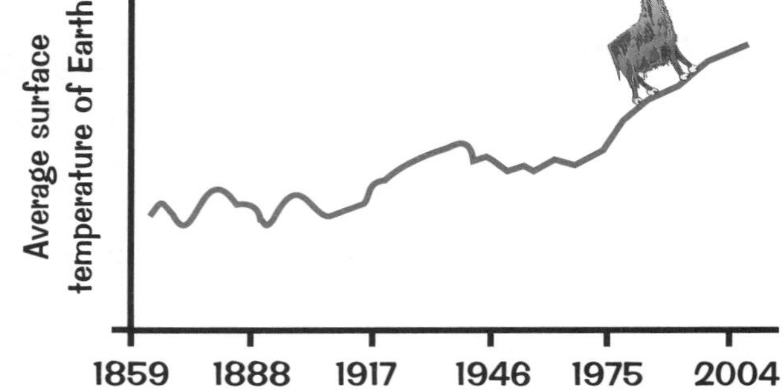

a) Describe the trend shown on the graph.

....

b) Suggest one reason for this change.

....

c) This graph shows how the current levels of three gases compare to their levels **before** the Industrial Revolution.

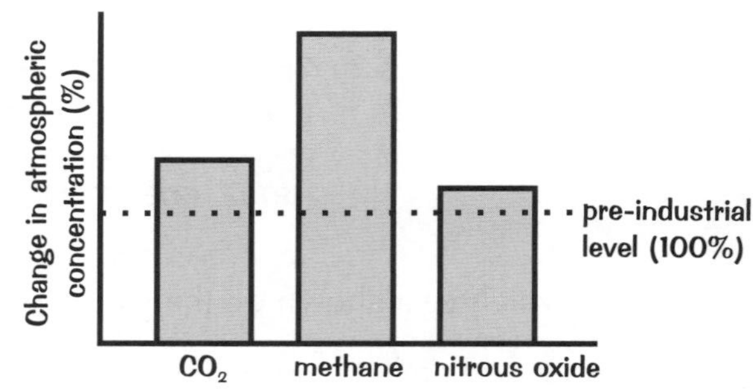

i) Which gas has had the **biggest** percentage increase in concentration? ....

ii) Give one source of this gas. ....

The Greenhouse Effect

Q3 **Deforestation** may increase the amount of **greenhouse gases** in the air. Fill in the gaps in the passage below to explain how this happens.

> Trees are burnt to clear land. This releases carbon dioxide into the .... At the same time .... feed on the bits of dead wood that remain and release carbon dioxide when they .... Trees normally take in carbon dioxide to use in .... If trees are cut down there will be less carbon dioxide .... from the air.

Q4 Human activity releases carbon dioxide into the atmosphere.

a) Give two examples of human activities that release carbon dioxide.

....

b) Which of these are reasons why forests are cut down? Tick the correct boxes.

- [ ] to get timber
- [ ] to clear land for farming
- [ ] to remove dangerous animals
- [ ] to clear land to raise animals
- [ ] to reduce the greenhouse effect.

c) Name a greenhouse gas other than carbon dioxide.

....

Q5 Underline the statements below about the greenhouse effect that are **true**.

The greenhouse effect is needed for life as we know it.

Greenhouse gases include carbon dioxide and sulfur dioxide.

The greenhouse effect causes acid rain.

Increasing amounts of greenhouse gases may lead to global warming.

Top Tips:

Climate change isn't a subject that scientists know all about. Ideas about what's happening and the possible long-term effects are evolving all the time, and it's hard to find two scientists that totally agree with one another. You've just got to be aware that there are different theories.

Climate Change

Q1 Which of these statements about global warming are **true**? Underline those that are.

The UK is definitely going to keep getting warmer.

If temperatures increase, sea levels will rise.

Droughts may occur more frequently in the future.

No one is sure what is going to happen.

Q2 These statements help explain how global warming may lead to **floods**. Use them to complete the **flow chart** below.

Low-lying areas might be flooded.

The seas get warmer and expand.

Sea levels start to rise.

Higher temperatures make ice melt.

1 ____________ 2 ____________

3 ____________

4 ____________

Q3 Scientists **collect data** to find out if climate change is really happening. Fill in the gaps in the passage below to explain what they are doing. You can use words more than once or not at all.

temperature	rulers	atmospheric	colour	speed	satellites	fridge

Scientists use .... to measure snow and ice cover and the .... of the sea surface. Features of ocean currents, such as their .... and their .... are recorded to see if they are changing. Automatic weather stations monitor .... temperatures.

Q4 One UK newspaper said that global warming will be good for the UK because people will be able to have more barbecues. Do you think this view is right? Explain your answer.

....

....

Q5 Two university students carried out **observations**. Student A noticed that a glacier was melting. Student B noticed that daffodils were flowering earlier in 2006 than in 2005. Both students concluded that this was due to **global warming**. Are they right? Explain your answer.

....

....

Sustainable Development

Q1 Match the words in the box to the descriptions below.

ecosystem	sustainable development	biodiversity

a) Meeting the needs of the current population without harming the ability of future generations to meet their needs. ....

b) The variety of plant and animal species in an area. ....

c) The environment and the living things in it. ....

Q2 Ecosystems like rainforests contain many different species. If we destroy rainforests we risk reducing biodiversity.

a) Explain what is meant by 'reducing biodiversity'.

....

....

b) If rainforests are destroyed, useful species may be lost. Give two things that could be obtained from species found in the rainforest and used by humans.

....

c) Describe another problem that may be caused by reduction of biodiversity.

....

....

Q3 **Lichens** are often studied to find out how much **air pollution** there is in an area.

a) What do we call an organism whose presence can give us information about pollution in an area?

....

b) The graph shows the number of lichens found in different areas.

Use the graph to help you decide if a high number of lichens indicates a badly polluted atmosphere or a clean atmosphere. Explain your answer.

....

....

Number of lichens
City
Countryside
Near a power station
Near a motorway
Area

c) Which organism could you look for to find out how polluted different rivers are?

....

Mixed Questions — Biology 1b

Q1 The graph shows how the **body temperatures** of a camel and a goat change throughout the day in a hot desert.

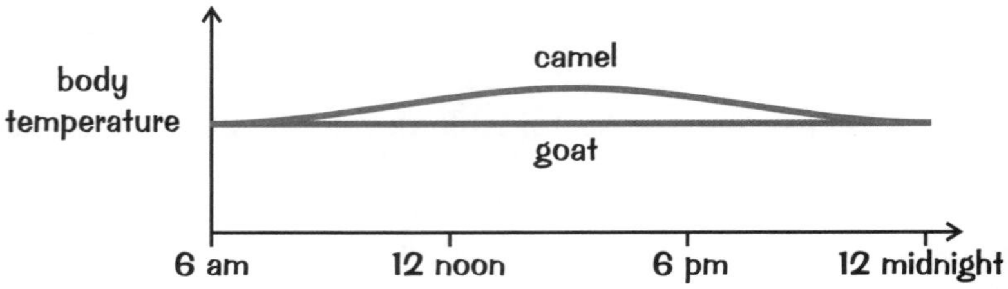

a) Between 6 am and 12 noon, what happens to the body temperature:

i) of the camel?

ii) of the goat?

b) Which one of the animals keeps cool by sweating?

c) Explain why animals that use sweating to keep cool can't survive well in deserts.

d) Camels were a traditional means of transport in the desert. However, more people are now using 4-wheel-drive jeeps. Explain why a camel is a **more sustainable** form of transport than a jeep.

Q2 The graph shows how the **populations** of snowy owls and lemmings in a community vary over time.

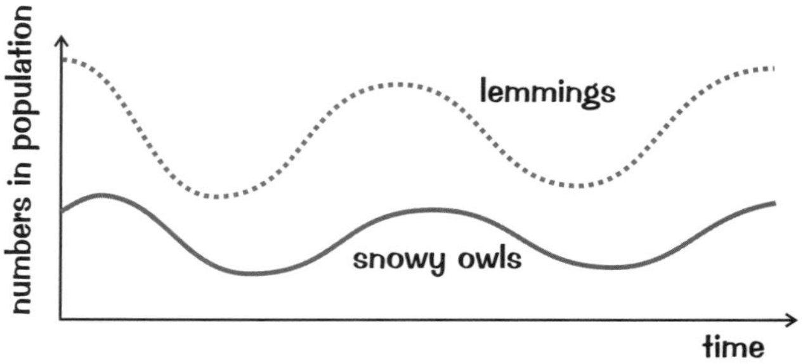

a) Just after the population of lemmings increases, the population of snowy owls increases. Explain why this happens.

b) Give one possible reason why the population of lemmings regularly increases.

c) Suggest why snowy owls have **white** plumage for part of the year but are **brown** at other times.

d) Most owls today have excellent night vision. However, many years ago, this sense was not so well developed. Explain how owls **evolved** this characteristic.

Mixed Questions — Biology 1b

Q3 The table shows the characteristics of four people, code-named **M**, **Q**, **X** and **Z**.

Characteristic	Code-name			
	M	Q	X	Z
They have a suntan	✓	✓		
They are male	✓	✓	✓	
They can roll their tongue	✓		✓	
Natural hair colour is brown	✓	✓	✓	✓
They have bleached blond hair			✓	✓
They have brown eyes	✓	✓	✓	

a) Who can roll their tongue and has a suntan? Code-name: ....

b) Which two features are caused by differences in the environment?

1. .... 2. ....

c) Which two people could be identical twins? Code-names: ....

d) The person code-named Z has diabetes. Explain how **genetic engineering** is used to help her.

....

....

Q4 An experiment was done with two **fertilised natterjack toad eggs**. The eggs came from completely different parents. The nucleus of **egg A** was put into **egg B**, and the nucleus of egg B was **removed** (see the diagram on the right).

A B

Nucleus from A is inserted into B

Nucleus from B is discarded

a) Egg **A** did not grow into a toad. Why not?

....

b) Egg **B** grew into a toad, but it looked like the parents of egg **A**, not the parents of egg **B**. Why?

....

....

c) Is this an example of sexual or asexual reproduction? Explain your answer.

....

d) Natterjack toad numbers have decreased dramatically over the last century. This is largely due to **human impact**. Suggest **two** ways that humans may have contributed to this decrease in numbers.

....

....

e) **Competition** with other amphibians has also had an effect on the number of natterjack toads. Suggest **two** things that the toads may have been competing for.

....

f) Because of their permeable skin, amphibians are '**sensitive indicator species**'. Explain what this term means. ....

....

Mixed Questions — Biology 1b

Q5 Gardeners can produce **clones** by taking '**cuttings**' from a plant. If they are kept in a damp atmosphere or in moist compost, the cuttings eventually grow roots and become new plants.

Tips are removed and grown in compost

a) What type of reproduction is involved in this method?

....

b) What does the term **clones** mean?

....

c) Why would a gardener want to produce clones of their plants?

....

....

d) A gardener produces some cloned plants. He notices that they all look **slightly different**. Explain why this is.

....

....

Q6 These graphs show the changes in **average temperatures** and **sea level** since 1880.

Change in temperature (°C): 0, 0.1, 0.2, 0.3, 0.4, 0.5, 0.6
1850 1875 1900 1925 1950 1975 2000
Year

Change in sea level (cm): -10, -5, 0, 5, 10, 15, 20
1850 1875 1900 1925 1950 1975 2000
Year

a) Suggest a reason for the general trend in temperature, using what you know about the **human impact** on the environment.

....

....

b) Explain why this temperature change is likely to have caused the change in sea level shown.

....

....

c) Underline the changes below that are likely to result from **global warming**.

The UK will have longer daylight hours | Ocean currents will be disrupted | More hurricanes | Oceans will dry up

d) Complete this short passage:

Global warming is likely to cause many species to become extinct. This means that fewer different species will be found in certain areas. This is known as a reduction in ....

Atoms and Elements

Q1 a) Name the three types of **particles** found in **atoms**.

....

b) Which two **particles** are only found in the **nucleus** of an atom?

....

Q2 Circle the correct words to complete these sentences.

a) Most of an **atom** is made up of empty space / electrons.

b) Most of the mass of an **atom** is due to the nucleus / electrons.

c) All the **atoms** of an **element** are the same / different.

d) To find out what **element** an atom is from, you look at the number of protons / neutrons.

Q3 Look at these diagrams of substances. Circle the ones that contain only **one element**.

copper oxygen water ethane

Q4 a) Draw a diagram of a **helium atom**.

b) Label each type of **particle** on your diagram.

Helium has 2 of each type of particle.

Q5 Many everyday substances, such as oxygen, gold and aluminium, are **elements**. Other substances such as water and sugar are not.

Explain what this means in terms of the **atoms** in them.

....

....

The Periodic Table

Q1 Draw lines to connect each **element** with its **symbol**.

copper	C	sodium	I
nitrogen	H	chlorine	Ca
carbon	Cu	sulfur	Cl
iron	Fe	iodine	Na
hydrogen	N	calcium	S

If you get stuck, you can always look at the periodic table (there's one at the front of this book).

Q2 Choose from these words to fill in the blanks. You do not have to use all the words.

left-hand **right-hand** **horizontal** **similar** **different**
vertical **metals** **non-metals** **transition**

a) A group in the periodic table is a .... line of elements.

b) Most elements are ....

c) The elements between group II and group III are called .... metals.

d) Non-metals are on the .... side of the periodic table.

e) Elements in the same group have .... properties.

Q3 Lithium is **less reactive** than sodium, which is **less reactive** than potassium. Use this information to decide whether these sentences are true or false.

	True	False
Reactivity increases as you go down group I.	☐	☐
Reactivity decreases as you go down group I.	☐	☐

Have a look at the positions of lithium, sodium and potassium in the periodic table.

Q4 Argon is an extremely **unreactive** gas. Use the periodic table to give the names of two more gases that you would expect to have similar properties to argon.

1. ....

2. ....

Compounds and Mixtures

Q1 State whether each of these diagrams represents an **element**, a **mixture** or a **compound**.

A	B	C
H H, N N, Cl Cl, N N	H H O, H O H, H H O	Na Na Na Na (×5 rows)

a) A .... **b)** B .... **c)** C ....

Q2 The **formula** of copper carbonate is $CuCO_3$.

a) How many **atoms** of **carbon** are shown in this formula?

....

b) Is copper carbonate a **compound**, an **element** or a **mixture**?

....

c) In total, how many **atoms** are shown in the **formula**?

....

Q3 Complete the table by putting the substances in the correct columns.

sugar, carbon monoxide, copper, sulfur, salt, air, gold, carbon dioxide, milk

elements	compounds	mixtures

Top Tips: Sometimes you'll see formulas for chemicals that you've never heard of. Don't get stressed out — the same rules for identifying the elements that are in them apply to them all. So once you've got the hang of some simple ones like H_2O, you'll be able to do them all night long.

Compounds and Mixtures

Q4 **Seawater** is a **mixture** of water and various dissolved substances, such as sodium chloride (table salt). **Water** is a **compound** of **hydrogen** and **oxygen**.

Are these statements true or false?

		True	False
a)	The substances in seawater are not chemically bonded to each other.	☐	☐
b)	Water can be separated into hydrogen and oxygen by boiling it.	☐	☐
c)	When seawater is heated until all the water evaporates, the only thing that is left behind is table salt.	☐	☐
d)	The formula for water is H_2O because it contains two hydrogen atoms joined to one oxygen atom.	☐	☐

Q5 Choose from these words to fill in the blanks. You may use some words more than once.

compounds, different, bonds, separate, electrons, elements, identical, taking

When atoms of different elements react they form bonds by giving away, taking or sharing .... The chemicals produced are called .... and are usually very difficult to .... using physical methods. The properties of compounds are .... from those of the elements used to make them. Mixtures are usually easier to .... because there are no chemical .... between their different parts.

Q6 The diagram shows some of the **atoms** in air.

a) In total, how many atoms are shown in the diagram?

....

b) What is the formula of the compound shown in the diagram?

....

c) Explain why the nitrogen in the diagram is not a compound.

....

Top Tips: Compounds always contain two or more different elements bonded together. Mixtures also contain two or more elements and the particles in them can be compounds. The difference is that mixtures contain at least two sorts of particles that are not chemically joined together.

Balancing Equations

Q1 This **equation** shows the formation of **carbon dioxide** when carbon is burned in air:

$$C + O_2 \rightarrow CO_2$$

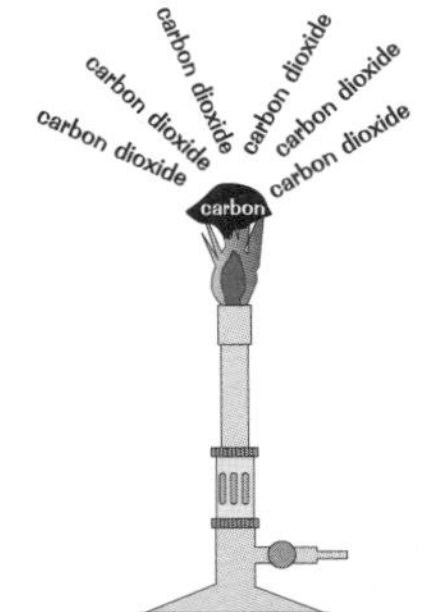

a) Name the **reactants** in this equation.

....

b) Name the **product** in this equation.

....

c) Explain why this equation is **balanced**.

....

Q2 Choose from these words to fill in the blanks.

compounds **colour** **state** **reactants** **mass** **size** **atoms**

In any chemical reaction the mass of the products is always the same as the .... of the .... This is because the .... that you start with are always still there at the end of the process, even if they are joined in different ways.

Q3 This is the **equation** for burning hydrogen in air.

$$2H_2 + O_2 \rightarrow 2H_2O$$

a) How many H and O atoms are shown on the **left-hand** side of the equation?

H .... O ....

b) How many H and O atoms are shown on the **right-hand** side of the equation?

H .... O ....

c) Is this equation balanced? Explain your answer.

....

Top Tips: The most important thing to remember with balancing equations is that you can't change the little numbers — if you do that then you'll change the substance into something completely different. Just take your time and work through everything logically.

Balancing Equations

Q4 Which of the following equations are **balanced** correctly?

		Correctly balanced	Incorrectly balanced
a)	$H_2 + Cl_2 \rightarrow 2HCl$	☐	☐
b)	$CuO + HCl \rightarrow CuCl_2 + H_2O$	☐	☐
c)	$N_2 + H_2 \rightarrow NH_3$	☐	☐
d)	$CuO + H_2 \rightarrow Cu + H_2O$	☐	☐
e)	$CaCO_3 \rightarrow CaO + CO_2$	☐	☐

Q5 Here is the equation for the formation of carbon **mono**xide in a poorly ventilated gas fire. It is **not** balanced correctly.

$$C + O_2 \rightarrow CO$$

Circle the correctly balanced version of **this** equation.

$$C + O_2 \rightarrow CO_2$$

$$C + O_2 \rightarrow 2CO$$

$$2C + O_2 \rightarrow 2CO$$

Q6 Write out the balanced **symbol** equations for the unbalanced picture equations below.

a) (Na) + (Cl Cl) → (Na Cl)

....

b) (Li) + (O O) → (Li O Li)

....

c) (Mg O O C O) + (H Cl) → (Cl Mg Cl) + (H O H) + (O C O)

....

d) (Li) + (H O H) (H O H) → (Li O H) + (H H)

....

Using Limestone

Q1 **Calcium carbonate** is the main substance in **limestone**. Its formula is **$CaCO_3$**.

a) Which three elements are in calcium carbonate?

....

b) How many atoms of each element are shown in the formula for calcium carbonate?

....

Q2 Limestone is a **sedimentary** rock which often contains **fossilised** shells and sometimes bones.

a) What process is used to extract limestone?

....

b) Give two uses of limestone.

....

Q3 Small pieces of limestone were weighed and then dropped into two beakers, A and B. Beaker A contained **distilled water** and beaker B contained **dilute hydrochloric acid**. After half an hour the pieces were removed, dried, and weighed again.

a) What would you expect to have happened to the mass of each block?

....

....

A
B
0.000
distilled water
dilute hydrochloric acid

b) Use the results of this experiment to explain why limestone buildings get damaged over time.

....

Q4 The hills of Northern England are dotted with the remains of **lime kilns** where **limestone** ($CaCO_3$) was heated by farmers to make **quicklime** (CaO). **Carbon dioxide gas** (CO_2) was also produced.

a) What is the chemical name for quicklime?

....

b) Write a word equation for the reaction that takes place in a lime kiln.

....

c) Quicklime reacts violently with water to make slaked lime, calcium hydroxide ($Ca(OH)_2$). Slaked lime is a weak alkali.

What do farmers use slaked lime for?

....

Using Limestone

Q5 Use the words below to fill the gaps in the passage.

sand sodium carbonate wood concrete clay limestone

Heating powdered .... with clay in a kiln makes cement.
When cement is mixed with water, gravel and sand it makes
...................................., which is a very common building material.
Heating limestone with .... and ....
makes glass.

Q6 This passage is about **limestone extraction** in the Peak District National Park.
Read the extract and then answer the questions that follow.

The Peak District National Park covers about 1500 km^2 of land. Tourism is very important — a lot of people visit the area to enjoy the countryside. Limestone quarrying is also part of the local economy and there are 12 large quarries in the park. Some people aren't keen on all this — they say that quarrying is spoiling the natural beauty of the landscape, and discouraging tourists from visiting.

The limestone in the Peak District is very pure. It has been used locally in agriculture, and burned in lime kilns, for many years. When canals and railways were built in the area, limestone quarried in the park could be taken further afield, for use in industries elsewhere. This continues today, and is another cause for concern — large lorries clog up narrow roads and disturb the peace and quiet in small villages.

A lot of limestone has been dug out of the Peak District. In 1990, 8.5 million tonnes of limestone were quarried from the Peak District National Park — more than five times as much as in 1951. This limestone is used in several different industries (the figures below are for 1989).

Use	Percentage
Aggregate (for road-building etc.)	55.8%
Cement	23%
Chemicals	17%
Iron and steel	4%
Agriculture	0.2%

Using Limestone

a) What makes the **limestone** in the Peak District particularly useful?

....

b) Approximately how many tonnes of limestone were quarried in 1951?

....

c) Describe one way in which limestone has been used locally in the Peak District.

....

d) State **three problems** that are caused by quarrying limestone in the Peak District.

1. ....

2. ....

3. ....

e) i) How was limestone originally **transported away** from the Peak District?

....

ii) How is limestone transported today?

....

f) Do you think that the person who wrote the article is in favour of quarrying or against it? Explain the reasons for your answer.

....

....

I ♥ Quarrying

g) Complete this table showing limestone extraction in the Peak District in 1989.

Use	Percentage	Total amount quarried in tonnes
Aggregate (for road-building etc.)	55.8%	(8 500 000 ÷ 100) × 55.8 = 4 743 000
Cement	23%	
Chemicals	17%	
Iron and steel	4%	
Agriculture	0.2%	

Using Limestone

Q7 Circle the substances that are **not** made with **limestone**.

glass quicklime plastic fossil fuel sandstone cement

Q8 Use words from the box to complete the sentences.

transparent cut concrete cheaper corrode

a) Cement is made from limestone and is used to make ....

b) Limestone is used as a building material more often than granite because it is .... and easier to ....

c) Glass is a useful building material because it is ....

d) Although concrete isn't as strong as most metals it is often used for building because it doesn't ....

Q9 In Norway **powdered limestone** is added to lakes that have been damaged by acid rain.

a) Name the process that takes place when the powdered limestone reacts with the acid in the lake.

....

b) Explain why powdered limestone is also used in the chimneys at power stations.

....

....

Q10 Limestone is a useful rock but **quarrying** it causes some **problems**.

a) Describe two problems that quarrying limestone can cause.

1. ....

2. ....

b) Explain how limestone quarries may benefit the local community.

....

....

Properties of Metals

Q1 Which of the following statements are true and which are false?

		True	False
a)	All metals are good conductors of heat.	☐	☐
b)	In the periodic table metals are on the far right-hand side.	☐	☐
c)	All metals are magnetic.	☐	☐
d)	Most metals can be bent and are strong.	☐	☐
e)	Only a few metals conduct electricity.	☐	☐

Q2 Suggest one important reason for each of the following facts:

a) Aluminium is used for making aircraft. ....

b) Lead is **not** used for making cars. ....

c) Copper is used for water pipes. ....

d) Potassium is **not** used for drink cans. ....

e) Steel (mainly iron) is used to build bridges. ....

Q3 This diagram shows the **structure** of a **metal**.

Label the **metal atoms** and the **free electrons**.

> ***Top Tips:*** Remember most elements are metals and most metals have similar properties. But don't be a fool and think they're all identical — there are lots of little differences which make them useful for different things. Some metals are pretty weird, for example mercury is liquid at room temperature, which means it's not ideal for making cars.

Properties of Metals

Q4 Most **metals** that are used to make everyday objects are found in the **central section** of the periodic table.

a) What name is given to this group of metals?

....

b) Why could metals from this group be used to make electrical wires?

....

Q5 This table shows some of the **properties** of four different **metals**.

Metal	Heat conduction	Cost	Resistance to corrosion	Strength
1	average	high	excellent	good
2	average	medium	good	excellent
3	excellent	low	good	good
4	low	high	average	poor

Use the information in the table to choose which metal would be **best** for making each of the following:

a) Saucepan bases ....

b) Car bodies ....

c) A statue to be placed in a town centre ....

Think about how long a statue would have to last for.

Q6 What **properties** would you look for if you were asked to choose a **metal** suitable for making knives and forks?

....

....

....

Top Tips: Ever wondered why we don't make bridges out of platinum? Cost is a big factor in the use of metals, so even if a metal is perfect for a job it might not be used because it's too expensive. The cheapest metals are the ones that are both common and easy to extract from their ores.

Metals from Rocks

Q1 Choose from these words to fill in the blanks.

metal oxygen rocks ore elements

a) .... are made up of minerals.

b) Minerals are solid .... and compounds.

c) A mineral that contains a useful amount of metal is called an ....

d) Metal ores often contain the metal combined with sulfur or ....

Q2 Draw lines to match these **metals** to the **ores** that they can be **extracted** from.

iron	chalcopyrite
aluminium	haematite
copper	bauxite

Q3 Most metal **ores** are extracted from the Earth from **mines**.
Describe **two benefits** that a mine can bring to an area and **two problems** that it can cause.

Benefit 1: ....

Benefit 2: ....

Problem 1: ....

Problem 2: ....

Q4 **Copper** is used to make electrical wires.

a) Give another common **use** of copper.

....

b) Copper can be extracted from its ore by reduction with carbon.
Why **can't** copper produced in this way be used for electrical wires?

....

c) How is copper that **is** suitable for making electrical wires produced?

....

Metals from Rocks

Q5 Copper objects such as old pipes can be **recycled**.
Give **two** reasons why it is important to recycle copper.

1. ....

2. ....

Q6 The following extract is taken from a press release from a scientific research company.
Read the extract and then answer the questions below.

> *Here at Copperextra we are very excited about our latest developments. Within six months we expect to be extracting pure copper from material that would usually be wasted.*
>
> *We are also making interesting developments in using bacteria for extraction. Using the latest genetic modification techniques we have developed a new strain of bacteria that can separate copper from copper sulfide at twice the speed of unmodified bacteria. In the future it should also be possible to use this technology to extract a range of other metals.*

Remember that the company are aiming to make money.

a) Why do you think the company is keen to develop a way of extracting copper from waste material?

....

....

b) Explain why using bacteria to extract copper from ores is more environmentally friendly than electrolysis.

....

....

Top Tips: Remember that metals are finite resources — there's a set amount on Earth and once we've extracted it all there won't be any more. We need to be able to get metals out of low-grade ores (ones that only contain small amounts of metal) to get enough to go round.

The Reactivity Series

Q1 Which of the following statements are true and which are false?

True False

a) Gold was found thousands of years ago because it exists naturally as pieces of uncombined metal. ☐ ☐

b) Calcium isn't very reactive so it was easy to discover. ☐ ☐

c) The least reactive metals are easiest to extract. ☐ ☐

d) When an ore is reduced, oxygen is added. ☐ ☐

e) Aluminium has to be extracted by electrolysis. ☐ ☐

Q2 **Iron** is extracted from its ore (iron oxide) in a blast furnace. **Carbon monoxide** formed in the furnace reacts with the iron oxide.

a) Write a **word equation** for this process.

....

b) What does the carbon monoxide do to the iron ore?

....

c) What is this process called? ....

Q3 When an **iron** nail is placed in a blue solution of **copper sulfate** ($CuSO_4$), the blue colour slowly fades and an orange-brown solid appears on the nail.

a) What is the orange-brown solid?

....

b) How can you tell that this reaction will take place just by looking at the reactivity series?

....

c) Write a word equation for the reaction.

....

The Reactivity Series

Q4 If zinc is heated with copper oxide this reaction happens:

zinc + copper oxide Þ copper + zinc oxide

a) Why does this reaction take place? ....

b) Would it be possible to produce zinc oxide by reacting zinc with aluminium oxide? ....

Explain your answer. ....

Q5 One of the first metals to be extracted from its ore was **copper**. The discovery may have happened when someone accidentally dropped some copper ore into a wood fire. When the ashes were cleared away some copper was left.

a) What was the source of carbon in the fire?

....

b) Why do you think that copper was one of the first metals to be extracted from its ore?

....

c) Many metals, like potassium and magnesium, were not discovered until the early 1800s. What had to be developed before they could be extracted?

How are they extracted?

....

Q6 Choose from these words to fill in the blanks.

below carbon more reduction electrolysis less above

.... can be used to extract metals that are .... it in the reactivity series. Oxygen is removed from the metal oxide in a process called .... Other metals have to be extracted using .... because they are .... reactive.

Top Tips: Stuff on the reactivity series isn't easy, so don't worry too much if you found these questions difficult. You don't need to learn the reactivity series off by heart — instead spend plenty of time making sure that you understand reduction, electrolysis and displacement reactions.

Making Metals More Useful

Q1 **Iron** is extracted from its ore in a **blast furnace**.

a) Name an **impurity** found in the **iron** produced in a blast furnace.

....

b) How does this impurity affect the properties of the metal?

....

c) If all the impurities are removed the iron is still not that useful. Why is this?

....

Q2 This diagram shows the arrangement of the **atoms** in **pure copper**.

Use the diagram to explain what happens when metals are **bent** into shape.

....

Q3 Most iron is made into an **alloy** called **steel**.

a) Write a definition of the term '**alloy**'.

....

....

b) How is **iron** turned into **steel**?

....

....

Tonight Matthew, I'm going to be... steel.

c) Why are **alloys harder** than **pure metals**?

....

....

Think about their atom arrangement.

Q4 Explain why **aeroplanes** are made from aluminium alloys rather than from pure aluminium.

....

....

Making Metals More Useful

Q5 Draw lines to connect the correct phrases in each column. One has been done for you.

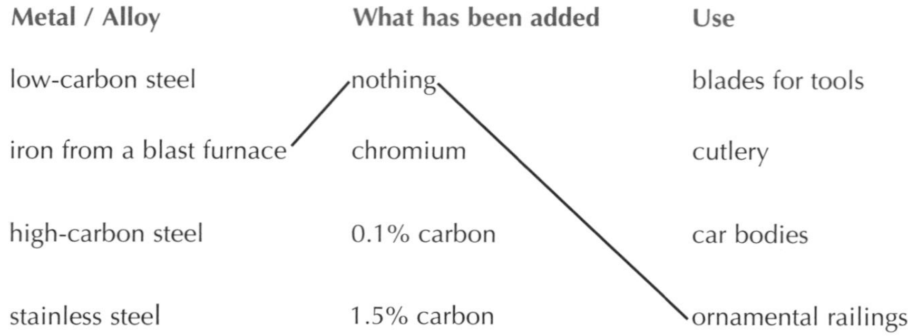

Metal / Alloy	What has been added	Use
low-carbon steel	nothing	blades for tools
iron from a blast furnace	chromium	cutlery
high-carbon steel	0.1% carbon	car bodies
stainless steel	1.5% carbon	ornamental railings

Q6 Complete the following sentences using the metals below.

gold copper silver nickel titanium

a) Bronze is an alloy that contains ....

b) Cupronickel, which is used in 'silver' coins, contains copper and ....

c) To make gold hard enough for jewellery it is mixed with metals such as ....

Q7 Materials called **smart alloys** have been developed.

a) What are **smart alloys**?

....

b) Give an example of a use for a smart alloy and explain what advantages it has over using ordinary metal.

....

....

....

Smart Alloy of the Month Award

Presented to: Nitinol

Presented by: CGP

Top Tips: As you must know by now, metals have lots of pretty useful properties, but they can be made even more useful by being mixed together to make alloys. Smart alloys are great for making those bendy glasses that don't break when you sit on them.

More About Metals

Q1 Aluminium is a useful metal.

a) Give two **properties** of **aluminium** that make it a useful metal.

1. ....

2. ....

b) Explain why it is **expensive** to extract **aluminium** from its ore.

....

....

Q2 Why is **aluminium** used to make **window frames**?

....

Q3 Explain why **aluminium** is **corrosion resistant** even though it is a **reactive** metal.

....

....

Q4 a) **Aluminium** and **titanium** are similar in some ways but different in others. Complete this table to compare the properties of **aluminium** with those of **titanium**.

Property	**Aluminium**	**Titanium**
Density	low	low
Reactivity		
Strength		
Corrosion resistance	high	high
Cost		

b) What **properties** of **titanium** make it particularly useful for making **artificial hip joints**?

....

Top Tips: Well, I hope you've had fun on this metals extravaganza. The good news is that none of this is too complicated — just make sure you've learnt the properties of the everyday metals like iron, aluminium and titanium and why they're so useful.

Fractional Distillation of Crude Oil

Q1 Crude oil contains **hydrocarbons**. What elements are **hydrocarbons** made up of?

....

Q2 Circle the correct words to complete this sentence:

Crude oil is **easy** / **difficult** to separate into its fractions because it is a **compound** / **mixture**.

Q3 Label this diagram of a **fractionating column** to show where these substances can be collected.

petrol **kerosene** **diesel** **oil** **bitumen**

These are in order of smallest to largest molecules from left to right.

Q4 What is the main **use** of each of these crude oil fractions?

a) Petrol ....

b) Kerosene ....

c) Bitumen ....

Q5 What is the connection between the **size** of the **molecules** in crude oil and their **condensing** (or **boiling**) points?

....

....

Properties and Uses of Crude Oil

Q1 **Crude oil** is a mixture of **hydrocarbons**. These **hydrocarbons** are mostly **alkanes**.

a) What are the names of the first **four** alkanes?

1. .... 2. .... 3. .... 4. ....

b) What **two** elements do alkanes contain?

....

c) These are two partially completed diagrams of the **structures** of two alkanes (all the carbon atoms are already shown). Complete the diagrams and write the name of each one.

```
    H
    |
C − C − H
```

```
|   |   |
C − C − C −
|   |   |
```

d) How many **bonds** do carbon atoms make?

....

The diagrams above should help you here.

e) The **general formula** for alkanes is C_nH_{2n+2}.
Use this formula to work out how many hydrogens an alkane with five carbons would contain.

....

Q2 There are some basic **trends** in the way that **alkanes** behave.
Circle the correct words to complete these sentences.

a) The longer the alkane molecule the **more** / **less** viscous (gloopy) it is.

b) The shorter the alkane molecule the **more** / **less** volatile it is.

c) A very volatile liquid is one with a **low** / **high** boiling point.

Q3 Each hydrocarbon molecule in engine oil has a **long** string of carbon atoms.

a) Explain why this type of oil is good for using as a **lubricant** in an engine.

....

b) Engines get very **hot** when they are in use. Why does this mean that oil molecules with a lot of carbon atoms are good to use as engine lubricants?

....

....

Using Crude Oil as a Fuel

Q1 Crude oil **fractions** are often used as **fuels**.

Give **four** examples of fuels that are made from crude oil.

....

....

Q2 As crude oil is a **non-renewable** resource people are keen to find **alternative** energy sources. What are the main **disadvantages** of each of the following energy sources?

a) **Solar** energy

....

b) **Wind** energy

....

c) **Nuclear** energy

....

Q3 Using oil products as fuels causes some **environmental** problems.
Explain the environmental problems that are associated with each of the following:

a) **Transporting** crude oil across the sea in tankers.

....

b) **Burning** oil products to release the energy they contain.

....

Q4 Forty years ago some scientists predicted that there would be no oil left by the year 2000, but obviously they were **wrong**. One reason is that modern engines are more **efficient** than ones in the past, so they use less fuel. Give two other reasons why the scientists' prediction was wrong.

....

....

....

Environmental Problems

Q1 Completely burning any **hydrocarbon fuel** will produce the same products.
Complete this word equation to show what happens when hydrocarbons are completely burnt.

hydrocarbon + ... → .... + ...

Q2 Sometimes **carbon monoxide** and/or **carbon particles** are produced when a hydrocarbon is burned. Under what **conditions** are these **pollutants** produced?

....

Q3 Explain why **sulfur dioxide** can be produced when hydrocarbons are burned.

....

Q4 Draw lines to link the correct parts of these sentences.

The main cause of acid rain is	acid rain.
Acid rain kills trees and	sulfuric acid.
Limestone buildings and statues are affected by	acidifies lakes.
In clouds sulfur dioxide reacts with water to make	sulfur dioxide.

Q5 Give three ways that the amount of **acid rain** can be reduced.

....

....

....

Q6 Why don't the **countries** that cause the most acid rain always suffer the most damage from it?

....

Top Tips: The best way to prevent acid rain damage is to reduce the amount of sulfur dioxide that we release into the atmosphere. When acid rain does fall there are some ways of reducing the amount of damage it causes, such as adding powdered limestone to affected lakes.

Environmental Problems

Q7 Circle the things that are significantly **increasing** the amount of **carbon dioxide** in the atmosphere.

burning gas | sunbathing | burning coal

drinking water | deforestation | driving cars | growing wheat

Q8 Explain some of the effects that many scientists believe an **increased** amount of **carbon dioxide** will have on the Earth.

....

....

Q9 Scientists are putting a lot of effort into developing **new fuels**.

a) Complete this table to show how three alternative fuels are produced:

Fuel	How it is produced
ethanol	
biogas	
hydrogen	

b) Which **two** of these fuels produce **carbon dioxide** when burnt?

....

Q10 Some scientists believe that the amount of **sunlight** reaching the Earth has decreased over the last 50 years.

a) Complete this passage:

The reduction in sunlight is called global .... This effect is caused by particles of .... produced when .... fuels are burnt. These particles cause more .... of sunlight back into space. They also help produce more ...., which also reflect sunlight.

b) Why do some people think that the evidence for global dimming is unreliable?

....

Environmental Problems

Q11 **Hydrogen** is often talked about as the 'fuel of the future'.

a) What is the **only product** produced when **hydrogen** is burned?

....

b) Explain why is it better for the **environment** if we burn hydrogen rather than petrol.

....

c) Currently, most of the vehicles that can use hydrogen as a fuel are demonstration vehicles that are being developed by scientists. Explain the problems that will have to be overcome before the public will be able to use hydrogen-powered vehicles on a large scale.

....

....

....

Think about storage of hydrogen and the costs involved.

Q12 Scientists are working hard to develop new **technologies** that are **environmentally friendly**.

a) Summarise the developments in technology in these areas that are helping to reduce environmental damage:

i) Sulfur emissions from power stations ....

....

ii) Carbon dioxide emissions from vehicles ....

....

b) List some ways that people can change their lifestyles so that they cause less environmental damage.

....

....

c) Do you think it is solely the responsibility of scientists to find ways of reducing environmental damage or should people be prepared to change their lifestyles too? Explain your answer.

....

....

Top Tips: Scientists are constantly looking at the ways people are damaging the environment and trying to come up with ways of reducing the damage. But different scientists have different opinions on issues like global warming and they don't all agree about what should be done.

Mixed Questions — Chemistry 1a

Q1 Describe each of the following substances as an **element**, a **compound** or a **mixture**.

a) Crude oil .... b) Copper ....

c) Aluminium .... d) Air ....

e) Water .... f) Glass ....

g) Calcium carbonate .... h) Carbon dioxide ....

Q2 The metals **aluminium**, **copper** and **iron** can be extracted from their **ores**.

a) Metal ores are often described as 'finite resources'. Explain the term '**finite resource**'.

....

b) Complete the following table by adding the **name** of a common ore of each metal and its **formula**. The first one has been done for you.

metal	name of ore	chemical formula of ore
iron	haematite	Fe_2O_3
aluminium		
copper		

c) i) Complete the word equation for the reduction of iron ore with carbon monoxide.

iron(III) oxide + ... → iron + ...

ii) The iron produced can be converted into the alloy called steel. Give **one** use of steel.

....

d) Copper metal can be extracted from its ore by **reduction** using carbon then purified by **electrolysis**.

i) Explain why electrolysis is used to produce copper metal for **electrical wiring**.

....

ii) Give **two** physical properties of copper that make it suitable for use in **electrical wiring**.

1. ....

2. ....

e) One of the most common elements present in the Earth's crust is aluminium.
Explain why aluminium metal can only be extracted using **electrolysis**.

....

....

Mixed Questions — Chemistry 1a

Q3 **Crude oil** is an important fossil fuel. It is a mixture of a large number of **hydrocarbon** molecules.

a) Briefly explain how crude oil is formed.

....

....

b) Explain the term 'hydrocarbon'.

....

c) Name one problem associated with the **transportation** of crude oil.

....

d) Name an **alternative fuel** to crude oil.

....

Q4 **Lubricating oils** in car engines keep moving metal surfaces apart. Viscous oils do this better than runny oils, but if they're too viscous they don't lubricate the moving parts properly.

The following experiment was set up to find which of two oils was the more viscous. The time taken for each oil to run through the burette was noted at two temperatures.

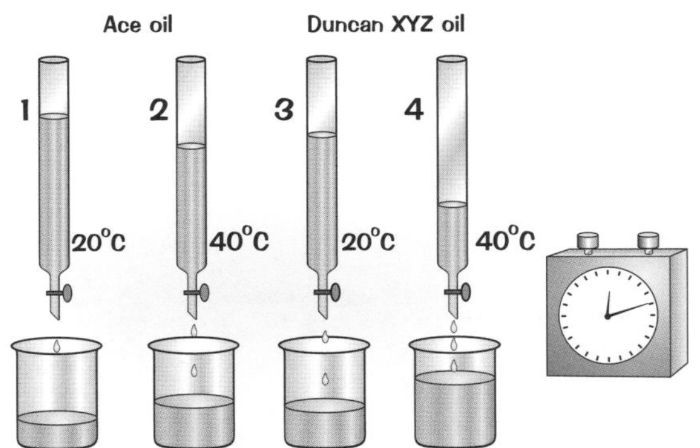

Burette	Temperature (°C)	Time for 50 cm^3 to flow through (s)
1	20	90
2	40	53
3	20	64
4	40	28

Use the table of results to answer the following questions:

The more viscous the oil, the longer it'll take to drip through the burette.

a) Which oil is **more viscous** at 20 °C? ....

b) Temperatures in an engine are much higher than 40 °C. What will happen to the viscosity of these oils at engine temperature?

....

c) How could you **improve** the experiment to find out which oil would be more viscous when used in an engine?

....

d) Which oil would you expect to be tapped off closer to the top of a fractionating column?

....

Mixed Questions — Chemistry 1a

Q5 Metals make up about 80% of all the elements in the periodic table.

a) Shade the area where **metals** are found on this periodic table:

b) Name the metal that's usually used for the following objects.
Choose from **steel**, **aluminium**, **titanium** and **copper**.

i) Car bodies ....

ii) Aircraft ....

iii) Hip replacements ....

iv) Electrical wiring ....

Q6 **Limestone** (calcium carbonate) is extracted by quarrying. When the **calcium carbonate** is heated strongly in a kiln, it will thermally decompose to form **calcium oxide**.

a) **i)** What is the **chemical formula** of calcium carbonate? ....

ii) Write a **balanced chemical equation** to show the formation of calcium oxide from calcium carbonate.

....

b) Give one use of **slaked lime** (calcium hydroxide).

....

c) Limestone is used in the manufacture of **cement**.

i) What is the other main ingredient of cement? ....

ii) Give an important use of cement. ....

d) Limestone is also used in the manufacture of **glass**.

i) Name the other two main ingredients of glass.

....

ii) By what simple process are these ingredients turned into glass?

....

e) The limestone of the Houses of Parliament is crumbling away.

What is causing the damage to the limestone and how?

....

Cracking Crude Oil

Q1 This diagram shows the cracking of kerosene into octane and ethene.

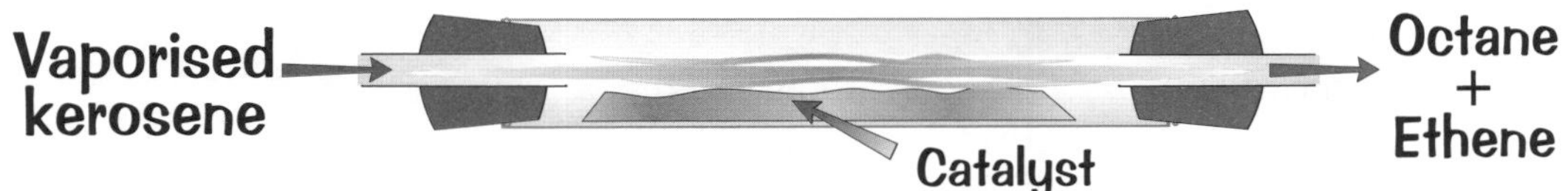

a) Circle the substance below which contains molecules with the longest carbon chains.

Kerosene **Octane** **Ethene**

b) What catalyst is used in cracking? ....

c) What **type** of reaction is cracking? ....

d) How many carbon atoms are there in the following molecules?

i) Kerosene ($C_{10}H_{22}$) .... **ii)** Octane ....

Think of the number of legs that an octopus has.

Q2 Fill in the gaps with the words below.

high	shorter	long	catalyst	cracking	diesel	molecules	petrol

There is more need for .... chain fractions of crude oil such as .... than for longer chains such as ....

Heating .... hydrocarbon molecules to .... temperatures with a .... breaks them down into smaller ....

This is called ....

Q3 Complete the equation below to show which **alkene** is formed.

$$C_{12}H_{26} \rightarrow C_4H_{10} + C_{.....}H_{.....}$$

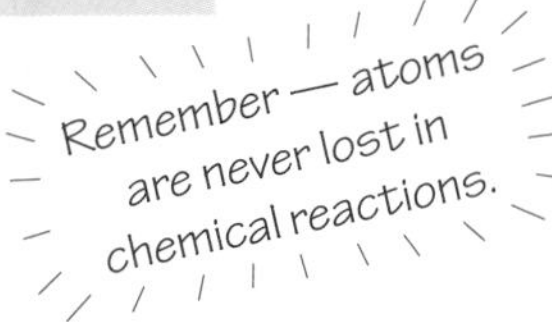

Q4 Name three useful substances that are produced when **diesel** is cracked.

1. ....
2. ....
3. ....

Alkenes and Ethanol

Q1 Circle the correct words to make the sentences below correct.

Alkenes are hydrocarbons with **single / double** bonds.

These bonds join two **carbon / hydrogen** atoms together.

Alkenes are known as **saturated / unsaturated** molecules.

Q2 Use the formula C_nH_{2n} to work out how many hydrogen atoms the following alkenes have.

a) Ethene C_2H.......... **b)** Pentene C_5H..........

c) Hexene C_6H.......... **d)** Heptene C_7H..........

Q3 Complete this table showing the molecular and displayed formulas of some **alkenes**.

Alkene	Formula	Displayed formula
Ethene	**a)**	$H_2C{=}CH_2$ (H and H on each C, C=C)
b)	C_3H_6	H–C(H)(H)–C(H)=C(H)(H)
Butene	C_4H_8	**c)**

Q4 There are two ways of making ethanol.
Sugar can be **fermented** using yeast, or **ethene** can be reacted with steam.

Tick the correct boxes to show which method each statement is about.

Statement	Fermentation method	Ethene method
needs high temperatures		
equipment can be simpler		
uses renewable resources		
produces more concentrated ethanol		
uses a catalyst (phosphoric acid)		

Using Alkenes to Make Polymers

Q1 Match each **monomer** with the **polymer** that can be made from it

styrene	poly(chloroethene)
ethene	poly(propene)
chloroethene	poly(styrene)
propene	poly(ethene) (polythene)

We bring you gold, frankincense... and poly-myrrh

Q2 Fill in the gaps in the passage below using the following words.

temperature **monomers** **different** **molecules**

Polymers are giant .... They are made by joining small molecules called .... together. Different polymers such as poly(ethene) and poly(propene) have .... physical properties. The physical properties of a polymer such as polyethene are affected by the conditions used when they're made, such as .... and pressure.

Q3 Slime is formed when **sodium tetraborate** is added to **poly(ethenol)**.

Which would make the **most viscous** slime when it is added to poly(ethenol)?
Circle the correct answer.

concentrated sodium tetraborate **dilute sodium tetraborate**

Q4 Tick the box next to the **true** statement below.

- ☐ The monomer of poly(ethene) is ethene.
- ☐ The polymer of poly(ethene) is ethane.
- ☐ The monomer of poly(ethene) is ethane.

Look really carefully at the spellings of the words.

Using Alkenes to Make Polymers

Q5 Below are some **properties** that polymers may have.

transparent | waterproof | hard-wearing | stiff | stretchy | non-conductor of heat | flexible

Select two properties that it would be important for a polymer to have for each of these uses.

a) Pairs of tights: .... and ....

b) Dental fillings: .... and ....

c) A jacket designed for hiking: .... and ....

d) A pan handle: .... and ....

e) A goldfish tank: .... and ....

Q6 Most polymers are **not** biodegradable.

Biodegradable means that something can rot.

a) What problems does this cause for the environment?

....

....

b) How can you minimise this environmental problem when using objects made from polymers?

....

....

Top Tips: It's amazingly easy to name polymers. You just take the name of the monomer (the little molecules that are joined together), stick it in brackets, and write the word 'poly' in front of it. And Bob's your uncle (except if his name's Mike or anything else that's not Bob).

Plant Oils and Emulsions

Q1 Match up the key words to their descriptions.

Nut	A machine that spins and separates crushed plant material.
Fuel	A seed with a hard shell.
Olive press	A process that removes water and impurities from the oil.
Centrifuge	A use for plant oils (apart from food).
Distillation	A machine used to extract the oil.

Q2 Oil can be extracted from some **fruits** and **seeds**.

a) Name two fruits and two seeds which are good sources of oil.

Fruits: .... and ....

Seeds: .... and ....

b) Unscramble the following. They are all things that vegetable oils in foods provide us with.

i) nivmitas ....

ii) sniteseal tatfy diacs ....

iii) genrye ....

Q3 Below are the stages of an experiment to extract the oil from olives.
Put numbers in the boxes to show the **order** they should go in.

☐ Separate oil from other liquids using a centrifuge.

☐ Crush the olives into a pulpy mush.

☐ Collect the liquid in a suitable container.

☐ Add masses to squeeze the oil out of the mush.

☐ Clean the outside of the olives with water and dry.

☐ Spread the olive mush between metal plates.

☐ Chop the olives and put the pieces in a mortar.

Plant Oils and Emulsions

Q4 Use the following words to complete the sentences below:

air dissolve suspended
moisturiser emulsion salad dressing

a) Oils don't .... in water, but the two can be mixed together to make an ....

b) Oil-in-water emulsions are droplets of oil .... in water. Water-in-oil emulsions are the opposite.

c) Some foods are emulsions, such as ...., sauces, milk and cream.

d) By whipping .... into emulsions, fluffy products like ice cream or whipping cream are created.

e) Emulsions are found in many non-food products such as ....

Q5 Each of these sentences has an error. Write out a **correct version** of each sentence.

a) Vegetable oils provide loads of energy, but are not nutritious.

....

b) Oily plates can be washed easily in just water.

....

....

Substances wash away easily in just water if they dissolve in water.

c) Emulsions are always formed from oil suspended in water.

....

d) The thicker an emulsion, the less oil it contains.

....

e) Emulsions can be combined with air but it makes them runnier.

....

Air is whipped into cream to make a topping for a trifle.

f) Emulsions are only found in foods.

....

Extracting and Using Plant Oils

Q1 Vegetable oils can be turned into fuels.

a) Name two vegetable oils that can be turned into fuels.

.... and ....

b) Why are vegetable oils suitable for processing into fuels?

....

Q2 Complete the passage using the words below.

crude oil	carbon dioxide	increase	plants

Burning biodiesel produces as much .... as burning normal diesel, but it comes from recently grown .... so it does not increase the overall level of this gas in the atmosphere.

Normal diesel is produced from ...., which is the remains of dead plants and animals from millions of years ago.

When burnt it causes an .... in carbon dioxide levels.

Q3 Show which of the following statements are **true** and which are **false**.

	True	False
In the UK biodiesel can't be made in large enough quantities to replace ordinary diesel.	☐	☐
Biodiesel is sold at every petrol station in the UK.	☐	☐
Diesel cars can run on biodiesel without any modifications.	☐	☐
New filling stations and pumps would need to be built for biodiesel.	☐	☐

Q4 Biodiesel is more 'environmentally friendly' than normal diesel or petrol. However, it is unlikely to replace them in the near future in the UK.

a) Give two reasons why biodiesel is more environmentally friendly than petrol or normal diesel.

1. ....

2. ....

b) Explain why biodiesel is unlikely to replace petrol or normal diesel in the near future.

....

Extracting and Using Plant Oils

Q5 Read this passage and answer the questions below.

Biodiesel is a liquid fuel which can be made from vegetable oils. It's renewable, and can be used as an alternative to ordinary diesel in cars and lorries etc. It can also be blended with normal diesel — this is quite common in some countries, such as France. You don't have to modify your car's engine to use biodiesel.

Biodiesel has several advantages. Producing and using it releases 80% less carbon dioxide overall than producing and using fossil-fuel diesel. So if we want to do something about climate change, using biodiesel would be a good start. Biodiesel is also less harmful if it's accidentally spilled, because it's readily biodegradable.

In the UK, we make most of our biodiesel from recycled cooking oils. But we don't make very much yet — you can only buy it from about 100 filling stations. The Government has been making some effort to encourage us to use more biodiesel. There's one major problem — it's about twice as expensive to make as ordinary diesel.

Most of the price you pay for petrol, diesel etc. is not the cost of the fuel — it's tax, which goes straight to the Government. Over the last decade, the Government has increased fuel taxes, making petrol and diesel more expensive to buy. Part of the reason they've done this is to try to put us off buying them — because burning fossil fuels releases harmful pollutants into the atmosphere and contributes to global warming.

So, to make biodiesel cheaper, in 2002 the Government cut the tax rate on it. The tax on biodiesel is now 20p/litre less than it is on normal diesel. This means that biodiesel is often a similar price to normal diesel. If the Government cut the tax even further, then people would be keen to use biodiesel, and more filling stations would start to sell it.

a) Name a country in which biodiesel is commonly blended with normal diesel.

....

Pay less tax — buy biodiesel

b) In the UK, what do we produce most of our biodiesel from at present?

....

c) Approximately how many UK filling stations stock biodiesel?

....

d) What did the Government do to try to encourage more people to start using biodiesel?

....

....

e) Describe the likely environmental impact if biodiesel were more widely used.

....

....

Using Plant Oils

Q1 Match up each label to a molecule.

Monounsaturated **Polyunsaturated** **Saturated**

```
    H   H   H   H   H   H   H
    |   |   |   |   |   |   |
H — C — C — C = C — C — C — C — H
    |   |           |   |   |
    H   H           H   H   H

    H   H   H   H   H   H   H
    |   |   |   |   |   |   |
H — C — C — C — C — C — C — C — H
    |   |   |   |   |   |   |
    H   H   H   H   H   H   H

    H   H   H   H   H   H   H
    |   |   |   |   |   |   |
H — C — C = C — C = C — C — C — H
    |                   |   |
    H                   H   H
```

Q2 True or false?

	True	False
Hydrogenation is when vegetable oils are reacted with hydrogen.	☐	☐
Hydrogenated fats melt at higher temperatures.	☐	☐
Margarine is a fully hydrogenated product.	☐	☐
Packets of biscuits often contain partially hydrogenated vegetable oil because it is cheaper than butter.	☐	☐
Trans fats keep your heart healthy.	☐	☐

Q3 Eating some types of fat is considered bad for your heart.

a) Why is it bad for your heart if you eat lots of saturated fats?

....

b) How do unsaturated oils such as olive oil and sunflower oil help your heart?

....

c) Explain why partially hydrogenated vegetable oils are thought to increase the risk of heart disease.

....

....

Q4 Ben and Martin both planned an experiment to identify saturated and unsaturated oils.

Ben's Method
1. Put some oil in a test tube.
2. Add some bromine water.
3. Shake vigorously.
4. Repeat for next oil.
5. When all the oils are done, write down the results.

Martin's Method
1. Put 2 ml of oil into a test tube.
2. Label the test tube with the name of the oil sample.
3. Add 5 drops of bromine water.
4. Record any colour change.
5. Repeat for each oil.

Whose experimental method is better? Give reasons for your answer.

....

....

Food Additives

Q1 Which of these statements about food additives are **benefits** and which are **drawbacks**? Put a **B** or a **D** in the box next to each sentence.

☐ Additives help food stay fresh.

☐ Additives can make foods look or taste better.

☐ Some additives can cause allergic reactions.

☐ Additives called stabilisers or emulsifiers are used to stop emulsions like mayonnaise from separating.

☐ There might be a link between some synthetic additives and hyperactivity in children.

☐ Chemical sweeteners are additives which mean people who have diabetes or who are on low-sugar diets can enjoy a wider range of foods.

☐ Additives, like gelatin or cochineal, can come from animals, so vegetarians may not want to eat foods that contain them.

Mmmm... E507, my favourite.

Q2 The table below shows some properties of tomato soup **before** and **after** additives are added.

	Colour	Texture	Sweetness	Shelf-life
Before additives added	orange	smooth	medium	5 days
After additives added	red	smooth	medium	12 days

Two different additives were added. Write down the type of each and explain why it is used.

Additive 1 — Type: ....

Reason for using: ....

Additive 2 — Type: ....

Reason for using: ....

Top Tips: Additives with E-numbers aren't always the evil things you might be led to believe they are. Take E300 (or ascorbic acid) for instance — this stops food going off as quickly. It sounds very unnatural and you might think that it's bound to be bad for you. But it's actually just vitamin C.

Food Additives

Q3 Fill in the gaps using the words below.

preserving	additives	safety tests	ingredients	salt
look	chemical	taste	E-numbers	texture

Before refrigerators were invented, people had to find other ways of .... food. One way was to use .... Nowadays we have a variety of compounds called .... that not only preserve foods, but can make them .... or .... different. Additives can also change the .... of foods. Most additives used in the UK have been given .... This shows they have passed .... Additives must be listed in the .... on a food packet.

Q4 Food colourings are usually made up of several different dyes. These can be separated out.

a) What is the name of the **separation** technique that allows us to examine the dyes used in foods?

....

b) Which dye is **more soluble**, A or B? ....

A

B

c) Which would travel more slowly, a **more soluble** or a **less soluble** dye?

....

Q5 Number the boxes to put the steps of this **chromatography experiment** into the right order.

☐ Measure how far each of the individual dyes has travelled and write this down.

☐ Add a spot of the dye you are testing to the pencil line on the paper.

☐ Place the paper into the solvent, not touching the bottom or sides of the beaker.

☐ Draw a pencil line about 1 cm up from the bottom of the chromatography paper strip.

Plate Tectonics

Q1 Do you know your evidence from your theories?
Write the letter **E** for evidence, or the letter **T** for a theory.

- [ ] Fossils of identical plants were found on either side of the Atlantic Ocean.
- [ ] Land bridges used to exist between continents.
- [ ] The coastlines of South America and South Africa seem to match like jigsaw pieces.
- [ ] Rocks with matching layers have been found on different continents.
- [ ] A 'supercontinent' used to exist 300 million years ago.
- [ ] Tropical plant fossils were found in the Arctic islands.

Q2 Identical animal fossils have been found at the opposite sides of oceans.

a) When this was first noticed, how did scientists explain it?

....

....

b) What was Wegener's rather different theory? ....

....

....

Q3 Sort these statements into reasons for **opposing** Wegener's theory and reasons for **supporting** it.
Write **O** for **opposing** or **S** for **supporting** in the box after each sentence.

Wegener's theory of moving continents sounded very strange. [ ]

Wegener had a PhD in astronomy, not geology. [ ]

Work done in the 1950s found that the ocean floors were moving in a similar way to continental drift. [ ]

Wegener had used inaccurate data in his calculations. [ ]

Wegener made incredible predictions that were proved impossible by scientific calculations. [ ]

In the 1960s geologists realised that mountains were created by chunks of land colliding. [ ]

Plate Tectonics

Q4 Below is a letter that Wegener might have written to a newspaper explaining his ideas. Use your knowledge to fill in the gaps.

Dear Herr Schmidt,

I must reply to your highly flawed article of March 23rd 1915 by telling you of my theory of .... Finally I can explain why the .... of identical plants and animals have been found in seemingly unconnected places such as .... and ....

The current idea of sunken .... between these continents is complete hogwash. I propose that South America and South Africa were once part of a much larger land mass that I have named .... This supercontinent has slowly been drifting apart over millions of years. The pieces are being pushed by tidal forces and the .... of the Earth itself.

I will shortly be publishing a full report of my scientific findings.

Yours faithfully,

A Wegener

Q5 True or false?

	True	False
Wegener found that each continent had its own unrelated collection of plant and animal fossils.	☐	☐
Animals were thought to have crossed between continents using land bridges.	☐	☐
The Earth's continents seem to fit together like a big jigsaw.	☐	☐
Rocks are made of layers, which are different on every continent.	☐	☐
Fossils of tropical plants have been found in places where they shouldn't have survived, like the Arctic.	☐	☐
Most scientists immediately agreed with Wegener's ideas.	☐	☐
Wegener had a PhD in geology.	☐	☐
Investigations of the ocean floor showed that although Wegener wasn't absolutely right, his ideas were pretty close.	☐	☐
Wegener died before his ideas were accepted.	☐	☐

The Earth's Structure

Q1 The Earth is not the same all the way through. It has a **layered structure**.

a) What is the **shape** of the Earth?

....

b) How thick is the **crust** on average? ....

c) Describe what the **mantle** is like.

....

....

d) Which **metals** are thought to make up the Earth's **core**?

.... and ....

Q2 True or false?

	True	False
The Earth is covered by large plates made from **only** the **crust**.	☐	☐
The tectonic plates move around because of **convection currents** in the mantle.	☐	☐
The plates move a few **metres** every year.	☐	☐
All of the plates are moving in the same **direction**.	☐	☐
Volcanoes are often found where plates meet.	☐	☐
Sudden plate movements cause **earthquakes**.	☐	☐

Q3 Scientists find it difficult to predict when earthquakes or volcanic eruptions will take place, but they can look for **clues**.

a) Describe one clue that scientists look for to try to predict if an earthquake is about to happen.

....

b) i) Describe one clue that a volcano may erupt. ....

....

ii) Why might this clue be a false alarm? ....

....

The Earth's Structure

Q4 The diagram below shows the boundary between the African and Arabian plates.

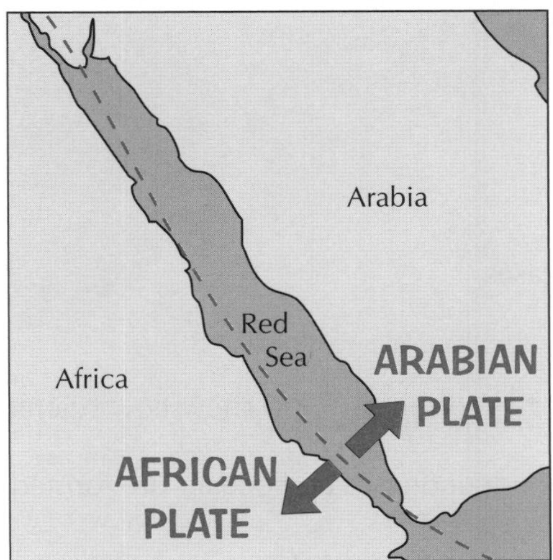

The Red Sea is widening at a speed of 0.000016 km per year.

Remember to include a unit in your answer.

a) At this speed, by how much will the Red Sea widen in 10 000 years?

....

b) At a certain point, the Red Sea today is exactly 325 km wide. If the sea level remains the same, how wide will it be at this point in 10 000 years' time?

....

Q5 The map below on the left shows where most of the world's earthquakes take place.

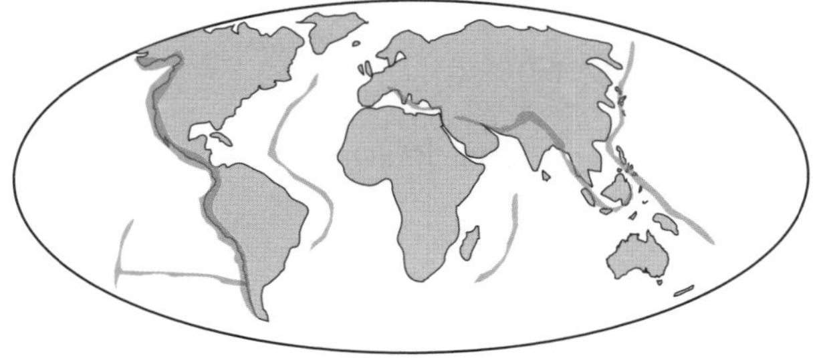

= main earthquake zones

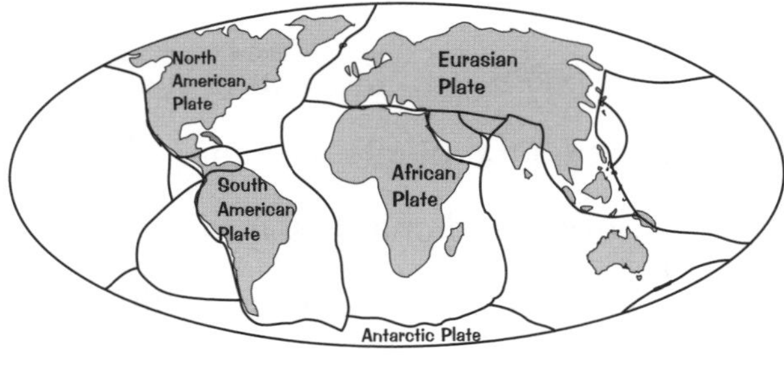

Compare this map to the one showing the tectonic plates.
What do you notice about the main earthquake zones?

....

....

The Evolution of the Atmosphere

Q1 This pie chart shows the proportions of different gases in the Earth's atmosphere today.

Add the labels:

Nitrogen

Oxygen

Carbon dioxide and other gases

Q2 Number these statements in the correct order to show how scientists think oceans were formed.

☐ The water vapour condenses and oceans are formed.

☐ The surface cools a little and a thin crust is formed. The volcanoes are still erupting.

☐ The Earth's surface is molten and there are many erupting volcanoes. Any atmosphere is "boiled away" into space.

☐ Water vapour and other gases are released and form an atmosphere.

Q3 Complete the passage with the words below to explain how the Earth's atmosphere has changed.

sedimentary **fossil** **carbon** **oxygen** **carbon dioxide** **photosynthesised** **atmosphere** **rises**

The atmosphere over two billion years ago had a lot of ....
Plants started to develop and spread rapidly. They .... and released .... into the atmosphere.
When the plants died the .... inside some of them was buried and changed into .... fuels.
When we burn fossil fuels this carbon is put back into the .... and the amount of carbon dioxide in the atmosphere ....

Q4 What were two effects of the **oxygen levels** in the atmosphere rising?

1. ....

....

2. ....

....

The Evolution of the Atmosphere

Q5 The noble gases make up about 1% of our atmosphere.

Underline the noble gases in the list below.

There are 6 of them.

oxygen **carbon** **radon** **argon** **nitrogen** **krypton**

fluorine **xenon** **chlorine** **helium** **neon** **iodine**

Q6 The noble gases are sometimes called the **inert gases**.

a) Explain why they are called this.

....

b) Write down a use of each of the following noble gases.

Argon: ....

Neon: ....

Helium: ....

Q7 Underline the correct answer(s) to each question.

a) Where are holes in the ozone layer mainly found?

Europe **North America** **Asia** **Antarctica**

b) Which gases break down ozone?

oxygen **CFCs** **nitrogen** **carbon dioxide**

c) Why is the ozone layer important?

It keeps the oxygen levels stable. **It has holes which let in the Sun's rays.**

It protects us from harmful UV radiation. **It provides protection from asteroids.**

d) The breaking down of the ozone layer is often linked to a rise in skin cancer.
Which **two** of the following may also be to blame for the rise in skin cancer?

more people sunbathing **more people cooking**

more people taking holidays in hot countries **more computer use**

Top Tips: Don't jump to conclusions — always look at the evidence suspiciously. For example, people in the UK used to have a week's hols in Skegness, if they were lucky. Now loads of people go to sunnier places for quite a few weeks every year. This trend might have been a bigger cause of the increase in skin cancer than the thinning of the ozone layer.

The Evolution of the Atmosphere

Q8 There is a theory that says that the water on Earth came largely from comets, not volcanoes.

Why is this theory not accepted by many scientists?

Think of different types of water.

....

....

Q9 The graphs below show the change in atmospheric carbon dioxide levels and the changes in average annual temperature since 1850.

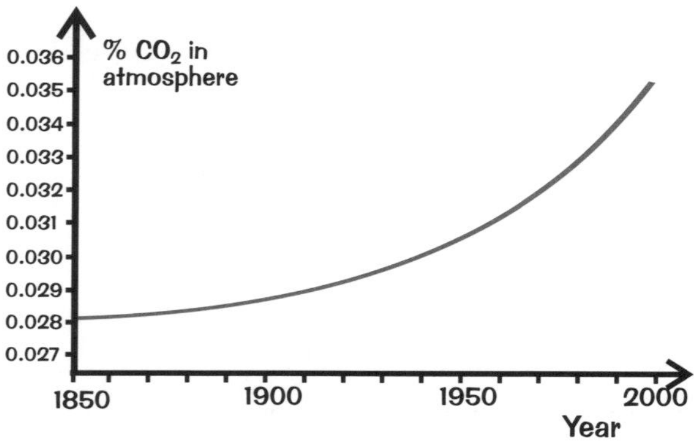

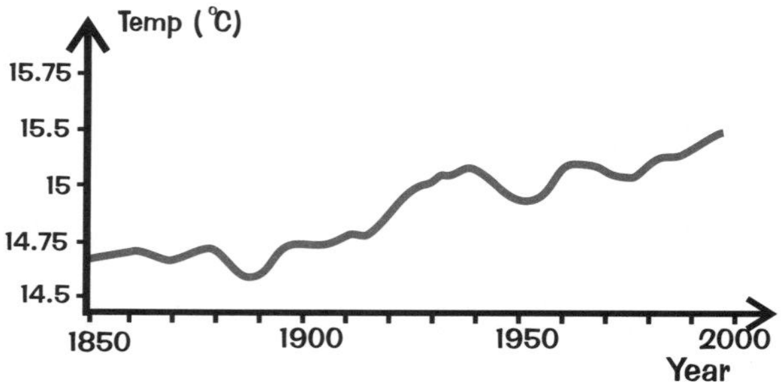

a) **i)** Name two human activities that are thought to have contributed to the rise in carbon dioxide levels over the last 150 years.

1. ....

2. ....

b) Do all scientists agree that the increased carbon dioxide concentration has definitely been caused by these human activities? If not, explain their reasons.

....

....

c) **i)** Look at the temperature graph. Has the temperature generally increased or decreased as the carbon dioxide level has risen?

....

ii) Many scientists believe that the temperature has changed because there is more carbon dioxide to trap the Sun's energy. What name is given to gases which trap heat from the Sun?

....

Mixed Questions — Chemistry 1b

Q1 Octane is heated and passed over a catalyst. It **thermally decomposes** as shown to the right.

octane → hexane + ethene

a) What is the process of splitting up long-chain hydrocarbons by thermal decomposition called?

....

b) Circle the correct structure of an ethene molecule.

A H₂C–CH₂ drawn as: H\ /H C–C H/ \H

B H\ /H C=C H/ \H

C H H | | H–C=C–H | | H H

D H H | | H–C–C–H | | H H

c) What can ethene be reacted with to make **ethanol**? Circle the correct answer.

warm water **carbon dioxide** **steam** **sugar**

d) Suggest **one** other way to make ethanol. What is the advantage of making it this way?

....

....

Q2 The diagram shows part of a long chain of **paper clips**.

a) Explain how the paper clip chain above is similar to a polymer.

....

....

b) Lots of **ethene** molecules can join together to form a useful long-chain polymer. What is this polymer called? ....

c) **Plastics** are polymers. Most plastics aren't biodegradable. Explain one problem this creates.

....

Q3 Use the information given in the first table to help you complete the second table below.

Plastic	Some properties
Poly(styrene)	Cheap, easily moulded, can be expanded into foam.
Poly(ethene)	Cheap, strong, easy to mould.
Poly(propene)	Forms strong fibres, highly elastic.
PTFE	Hard, waxy, things do not stick to it.
Perspex	Transparent, easily moulded, does not easily shatter.

Job	Plastic	Reason
a) Carpet		
b) Picnic glasses		
c) Insulating material		
d) Yoghurt cartons		
e) Non-stick frying pans		

Mixed Questions — Chemistry 1b

Q4 The ingredients list from a tin of macaroni cheese is shown below.

Another situation where stabilisers would have held everything together.

> **Macaroni Cheese — Ingredients**
> Water, Durum Wheat, Cheddar Cheese, Rapeseed Oil, Salt, Sugar, Skimmed Milk Powder, Mustard, Stabilisers (Polyphosphates, Sodium Phosphate), Flavour Enhancer (E621), Colour (E160)

a) Explain why the following have been added to the macaroni cheese.

i) sodium phosphate ....

ii) E160 ....

b) The macaroni cheese contains two additives that have E-numbers. What do E-numbers show?

....

c) The macaroni cheese contains rapeseed oil, which is a vegetable oil.
It is mostly a **monounsaturated** oil. Tick the true sentences below.

☐ The carbon chains in rapeseed oil do not contain any C=C double bonds.

☐ The carbon chains in rapeseed oil mostly contain one C=C double bond.

☐ The carbon chains in rapeseed oil mostly contain more than one C=C double bond.

d) Circle the correct word(s) to complete this sentence.

Rapeseed oil will / will not decolourise bromine water.

e) **i)** Which ingredient in the macaroni cheese is likely to contain the most saturated fat?

....

Animal products tend to contain more saturated fat.

ii) Name a **health problem** that too much saturated fat can cause?

....

iii) Vegetable oils can be mixed with water to form **emulsions**.
Give two examples of foods that contain emulsions.

....

Q5 People used to think that the Earth's surface was all one piece. Today, we think it's made up of separate plates of rock. One piece of evidence for this is fossils that were found in South America and Africa.

a) Give one other piece of evidence and say how it supports the theory.

....

....

b) What is thought to cause the **movement** of the plates?

....

c) Name **two** types of natural disaster that can occur at the boundaries between plates.

.... and ....

Mixed Questions — Chemistry 1b

Q6 The graphs below give information about the Earth's atmosphere millions of years ago and today.

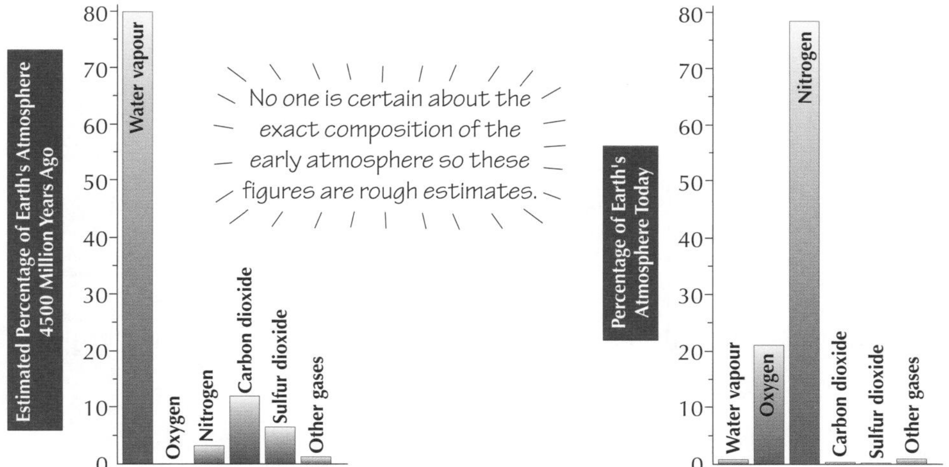

As you can see from the graphs, the Earth's atmosphere has changed quite a lot. Answer these questions about the changes.

a) Could the early atmosphere **support life** as we know it? Explain your answer.

....

....

b) About 3 billion years ago simple organisms started to **photosynthesise**. Which gas did this remove from the early atmosphere? ....

c) Even though the level of **carbon dioxide** is much lower now than millions of years ago, in the last 250 years the level has **increased**. Complete the following passage by circling the correct words.

> Humans are **increasing / decreasing** the amount of **carbon dioxide / oxygen** in the atmosphere by **burning / creating** fossil fuels. Also, deforestation **reduces / increases** the amount of carbon dioxide **absorbed / released** from the atmosphere.

d) i) **Biodiesel** is a renewable fuel. What is it made from? ....

ii) Explain why burning biodiesel produces **no net increase** in atmospheric carbon dioxide.

....

....

iii) Give one reason why biodiesel isn't widely used at the moment.

....

e) Tick the correct boxes to indicate whether each statement is **true** or **false**.

	True	False
i) 5% of the atmosphere is noble gases.	☐	☐
ii) The amount of ozone in the ozone layer is decreasing.	☐	☐
iii) Very early in Earth's history volcanoes gave out gases.	☐	☐
iv) Scientists are good at predicting volcanoes and earthquakes.	☐	☐

Heat Transfer

Q1 Draw arrows to match each method of heat transfer with the correct sentence.

Radiation — It only happens in liquids and gases.

Conduction — It does not need particles.

Convection — It is the main way heat is transferred in solids.

Q2 Complete the sentences below, using words from the list. (You may use words more than once.)

cooler **hotter** **transfer**

Heat flows from .... places to .... places.
This process is called heat .... When objects lose heat energy they get .... When they gain heat energy they get ....

Q3 Cars get hot if they are left out in the sun all day. Circle the correct explanation of **why** this is.

A The car absorbs radiation from the Sun, but does not emit any energy.

B The car emits more radiation to the air than it absorbs from the Sun.

C The car absorbs more radiation from the Sun than it emits to the surrounding air.

Q4 The sentence below contains two mistakes. Write out a correct version.

Infrared radiation is emitted from the centre of hot solid objects, but not from liquids or gases.

....

Q5 Three flasks, each containing 100 ml of water, are placed in closed boxes. Each flask and each box are at different temperatures.

A: Air in box 55°C; Water 60°C

B: Air in box 50°C; Water 65°C

C: Air in box 65°C; Water 70°C

Which flask will cool fastest?
Give a reason for your answer.

Flask .... will cool fastest because ....

....

Heat Radiation

Q1 Choose from these words to fill in the blanks. You do not have to use all the words.

shiny	not shiny	absorb	reflect

A 'matt' surface is a surface that's .... Dark, matt surfaces .... and emit lots of heat radiation. Light, glossy, and silvery surfaces .... most of the radiation that reaches them.

Q2 Draw arrows to match up each design feature with the reason for it.

A coolbag is lined with white or shiny silver material...

A wood-burning stove is painted matt black...

A survival blanket is shiny silver...

A solar panel is painted matt black...

...to keep heat in.

...to keep heat out.

...to let heat in.

...to let heat out.

Q3 Asma fills a **matt black** test tube and a **shiny silver** test tube with equal volumes of boiling water. She takes the temperature of the water in each test tube every 30 seconds as it cools down.

Which test tube will cool down faster? Give a reason for your answer.

....

....

Q4 Give a reason why steel **electric kettles** are often made very **shiny**.

....

....

Q5 Tick the correct boxes below to show whether the sentences are true or false.

		True	False
a)	The amount of heat radiation absorbed by a surface depends only on its colour.	☐	☐
b)	The hotter a surface is, the more heat it radiates.	☐	☐
c)	Good absorbers of heat are also good emitters of heat.	☐	☐
d)	Thermos flasks can keep hot things hot but cannot keep cold things cold.	☐	☐
e)	Silver survival blankets help the body to absorb heat.	☐	☐

Heat Conduction

Q1 Use these words to fill in the blanks in the passage below.

particles conduction kinetic energy vibrate hot

If one end of a short metal bar is heated, the other end of the bar will soon get .... too. This happens because heat makes the .... in the bar .... more and pass extra .... on to their neighbours. This is called .... In this way, heat spreads throughout the whole bar.

Q2 Most **metals** are **good** conductors of heat and most **non-metals** are **poor** conductors of heat. Liquids and gases are generally **worse** conductors than solids.

Write each of the following materials in the correct column of the table.

copper steel plastic air wood iron water aluminium

Good Conductors	Poor Conductors

Q3 Circle the correct words to complete these sentences.

a) The bottom of a saucepan is made of a good conductor so it **keeps** / **lets** heat in.

b) Saucepan handles are often made of a poor conductor so they transfer heat **quickly** / **slowly**.

c) Blankets are made from materials which conduct heat **well** / **poorly** and keep warmth in.

d) Central heating radiators are made of a **good** / **poor** conductor so that they **keep** / **let** heat out.

Think about this — in a car, the radiator is there to stop the engine overheating.

Q4 George picks up a piece of wood and a metal spoon. Both have the same temperature: 20 °C.

Explain why the metal spoon feels **colder** to the touch than the piece of wood.

....

....

Heat Convection

Q1 These sentences describe how a hot water tank gets hot, but they are in the wrong order. Number them 1 to 5 to show the correct order.

☐ Hot water rises to the **top** of the tank.

☐ Heater coils heat up the cold water by **conduction**.

☐ Initially, the water is **cold** and **dense**.

☐ The water gets hotter, so it expands and becomes **less dense**.

☐ This moving hot water displaces cold water and sets up a **convection current**.

hot water

heater coils

cold water

Q2 Fill in the blanks, using the words given.

solids	particles	move	hotter	cooler	heat energy

Convection happens in liquids and gases because their .... can .... easily from hot regions to .... regions, taking their .... with them. This cannot happen in ....

Q3 a) Tick the correct boxes to show whether the sentences are true or false.

	True	False
i) Usually, the cooler a liquid or gas is, the denser it is.	☐	☐
ii) If you only want a small volume of hot water, you should place the immersion heater near the bottom of the hot water tank.	☐	☐
iii) Heat reaches us from the Sun by convection.	☐	☐
iv) Convection currents can happen in water but not in air.	☐	☐

b) Write a correct version of each false sentence in the space below.

....

....

....

Q4 Match each observation with an explanation.

The very bottom of a hot water tank stays cold...

Warm air rises...

A small heater can send heat all over a room...

because water doesn't conduct much heat.

because heat flows from warm places to cooler ones.

because it is not so dense.

Useful Heat Transfers

Q1 Kabir heats a saucepan of water on an electric ring.

On diagram A, add 2 more labels to show useful heat transfers taking place.
On diagram B, add 3 labels to show non-useful (unwanted) heat transfers.

A — Useful Heat Transfers

B — Unwanted Heat Transfers

For a start, the pan is hot, so it's going to lose heat to the surrounding air by radiation.

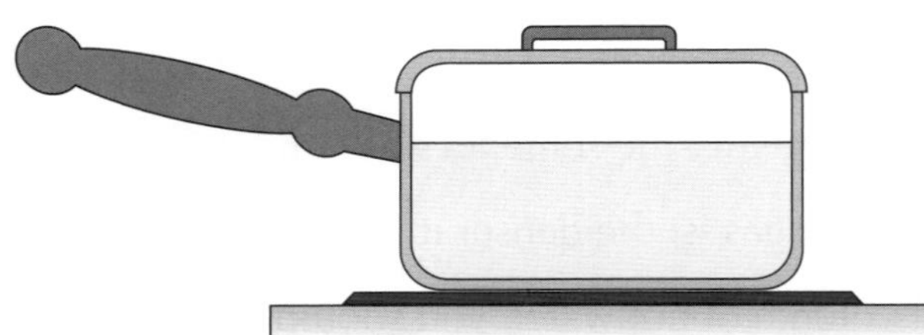

Q2 a) Complete the table to explain some features of a good saucepan in terms of heat transfer.

Feature	What it does	How it does it
Bottom made of copper.	Increases useful heat transfer.	Copper is a good conductor of heat.
Lid made of glass or plastic.		
	Decreases non-useful heat transfer.	Reduces conduction along handle.
Shiny outer surface.		

b) Why is it important to reduce non-useful heat transfers from the pan?

....

Useful Heat Transfers

Q3 Mr Jackson designed a wood-burning stove for his living room.

↑ to chimney

Explain why he decided to:

a) paint the outside with matt black paint.

....

b) make the door handles out of metal instead of wood, even though wood is less conductive.

What happens to wood when it gets really hot? — and why did cavemen sit around rubbing two sticks together?

....

Q4 Natasha did an experiment to test how well plastic foam keeps a beaker of water hot.

She put different thicknesses of foam around three beakers.
The water in each beaker started off at 100 °C.

After 10 minutes Natasha read the temperatures. Her results are shown on the diagram below.

Beaker	Temperature	Foam
A	60 °C	Foam 0.5 cm thick.
B	80 °C	Foam 1 cm thick.
C	90 °C	Foam 2 cm thick.

foam

hot water

a) Write down **two things** Natasha's results tell her about the effectiveness of the plastic foam.

....

....

b) In Natasha's experiment, what was:

This is the thing you measure.

i) the dependent variable? ....

ii) the independent variable? ....

This is the thing you change.

c) Natasha's investigation did not include a **control** beaker — one without any plastic foam. Why would a control beaker have been useful?

....

....

Energy Transfer

Q1 Write down the correct type of energy next to each example.

	Type of Energy
Stored in a battery.	
Possessed by hot water.	
Released by a nuclear reaction.	
Stored in a wound-up watch spring.	
From someone speaking.	

Q2 Which is the 'odd one out' in each list below?
Explain your answers.

a) Chemical energy, light energy, kinetic energy, sound energy.

The 'odd one out' is .... energy, because ....

....

b) A stretched bowstring, a battery, a wound-up clock spring, a stretched elastic band.

The 'odd one out' is .... because ....

....

Q3 Explain why:

a) **Gravitational potential** energy is sometimes called 'uphill energy'.

....

b) We should all try to **conserve energy** by using less oil, coal and gas.

....

c) The **total** amount of energy in the entire physical universe can never increase.

....

Q4 Complete the following **energy transfer diagrams**. The first one has been done for you.

			→	
	A solar water heating panel:	light energy	→	heat energy
a)	A gas cooker:	....	→	heat energy
b)	An electric buzzer:	electrical energy	→	....
c)	A television screen:	....	→	....

Efficiency of Machines

Q1 A central heating boiler uses the chemical energy in gas to heat up water for Freddie's bath. But some of the heat that's generated is **wasted** — it goes up the chimney.

On the diagram, label the **energy input**, the **useful energy output**, and the **waste energy.**

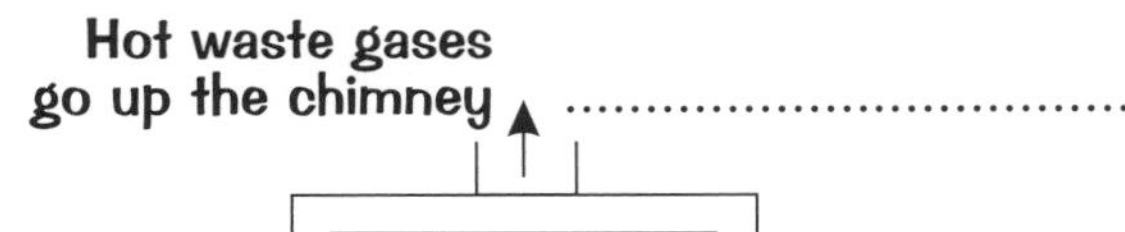

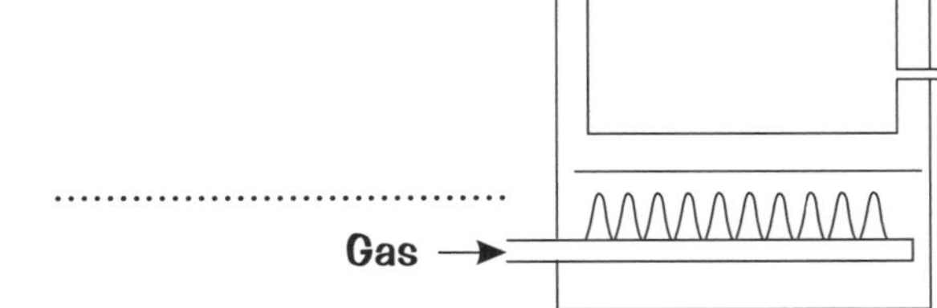

Hot water

Q2 Draw arrows to match up the beginnings and ends of these sentences.

A **machine** is a useful device which...

Whenever a machine **converts energy**...

Devices that are **more efficient**...

some energy is **wasted**, often as heat.

waste less energy.

converts energy from one form into another.

Q3 Tick the boxes to show whether these statements are true or false.

		True	False
a)	The total energy supplied to a machine is called the **total energy input**.	☐	☐
b)	The **useful energy output** of a machine is never more than its total energy input.	☐	☐
c)	The **wasted energy** from a machine is the energy it delivers that's not useful.	☐	☐
d)	The more **efficient** a machine is, the more energy it **wastes**.	☐	☐

Q4 Use the **efficiency formula** (or the nice **triangle**) to complete the table.

Efficiency = Useful Energy Output ÷ Energy Input

Total Energy Input (J)	Useful Energy Output (J)	Efficiency
2000	1500	
	2000	0.50
4000		0.25
600	200	

Top Tips: Efficiency is always a number between 0 and 1. If you get a number greater than 1, it means you've done your division upside down — oops. (Sometimes, efficiency is given as a %.)

Efficiency of Machines

Q5 Fill in the gaps. Use each word once.

heat efficient heaters useful wasted

No device is ever 100% .... One possible exception is electric .... The output from them is always .... because their job is to convert electrical energy into .... energy, so none is ....

Q6 Match up the beginnings and ends of the sentences.

For energy to be **useful** ...	...always ends up as **heat energy**.
We say energy is "always **conserved**" because the total amount ...	...it must be **concentrated**.
Eventually, all the energy supplied to a **machine** ...	...is always the same before and after.

Q7 Mrs Smith is choosing an electric kettle. She narrows the choice down to the two kettles shown here.

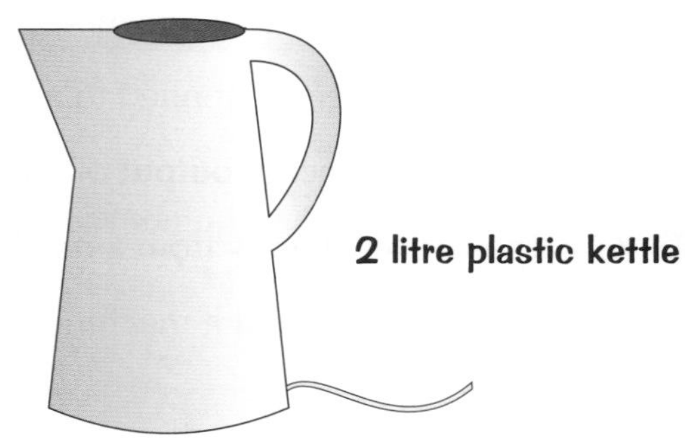

Write down five things Mrs Smith should consider when she decides which kettle to buy.

1) ....

2) ....

3) ....

4) ....

5) ....

Efficiency of Machines

Q8 Sajid hopes his new MP3 player is better than his old one. He decides to test which one is more **efficient**.

He puts new batteries in both MP3 players and switches them on. Then he times how long they each play for before the batteries run out.

a) Why does Sajid use new batteries?

....

b) How can he measure the **useful energy outputs**?

....

c) Write down one thing Sajid must do to make it a **fair test**.

....

d) Player A lasts for 3 hours and Player B lasts for 4 hours. Write a **conclusion** for Sajid's experiment.

....

Q9 Clive is researching different kinds of electric light bulb. He finds the following information.

	Low-energy bulb	Ordinary bulb
Electrical energy input per second (J)	15	60
Light energy output per second (J)	1.4	1.4
Cost to buy	£3.50	50p
Typical expected lifetime	8 years	1 year
Estimated annual running cost	£1.00	£4.00

Hint — most people don't like wasting money.

a) Write down two reasons for choosing a **low-energy** light bulb.

1. ....

2. ....

b) Write down two reasons why Clive might prefer to buy an ordinary bulb.

1. ....

2. ....

Top Tips: There's often more to choosing a light bulb in real life. For example, you might put an ordinary bulb in a room you rarely use, because the running costs would be so tiny that any savings would never pay back the extra cost of buying a low-energy bulb.

Energy Transformations

Q1 Indicate which of the following are true and which are false.

		True	False
a)	A television set is an **energy-converting device**.	☐	☐
b)	All **electrical devices** change some energy into heat.	☐	☐
c)	It is **not possible** to convert electrical energy into chemical energy.	☐	☐
d)	All types of energy can be measured in **joules**.	☐	☐

Q2 Write down the names of three devices used for **electricity generation**.

1) .... 2) .... 3) ....

Q3 Complete the following sentence.

A **battery charger** converts .... energy into

.... energy and .... energy.

Hint — the charger usually gets a bit hot after a while.

Q4 When an archer shoots an arrow into the air several **energy transformations** take place. The table below shows these transformations, but in the wrong order.

Number the energy transformations from 1 to 5 to show the correct order.

Order	Energy transformation
	Energy stored in the pulled bow and string is converted into kinetic energy.
	The arrow loses gravitational potential energy and gains kinetic energy as it falls to earth.
	Chemical energy in the archer's muscles is converted into elastic potential energy.
1	Chemical energy from the archer's food is stored in his muscles.
	As it goes upwards the arrow loses kinetic energy and gains gravitational potential energy.

Q5 Sarah eats three slices of **toast and jam** before riding her bicycle to work. Describe the **energy transformations** that take place as Sarah cycles to work. (The route she takes is completely flat.)

Don't forget about the energy that's wasted.

....

....

....

....

Energy Transformation Diagrams

Q1 Complete the following sentences by filling in the missing words.

In a **Sankey diagram** the amount of energy is shown by the .... of the arrow. The .... the arrow, the more energy it represents. The arrow representing the **input energy** is always .... than the one representing the **useful output energy**.

Q2 Here is a sketched Sankey diagram of the **energy transformations** in a **lamp**.

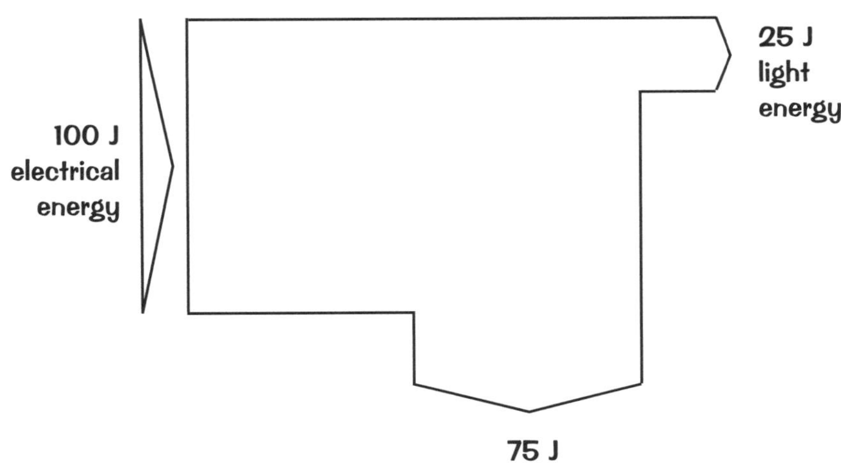

a) What **form** of energy is **wasted**?

....

b) What form of energy is the **useful output**?

....

Q3 This diagram shows the energy changes in a **toy crane**. The diagram is drawn to scale.

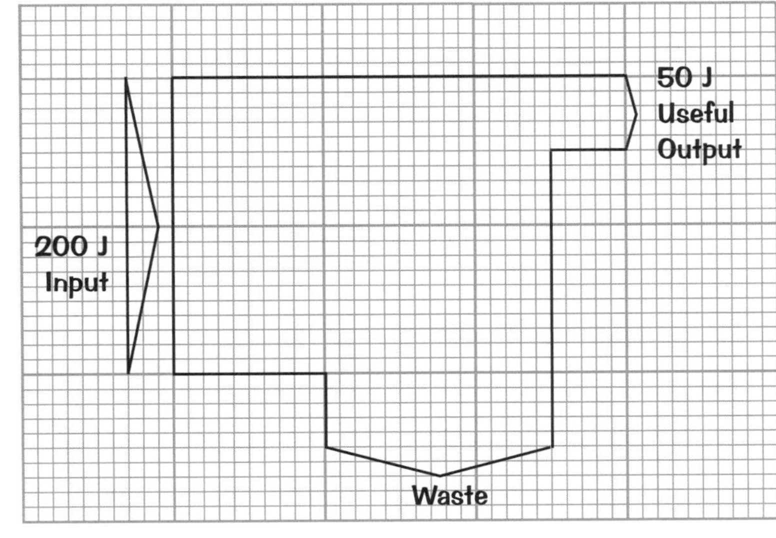

a) How much energy is **one small square** worth? .... J

b) How much energy is **wasted**? .... J

Energy Transformation Diagrams

Q4 Professor Bean is testing a new **high-efficiency** car engine.

He finds that for every 100 J of energy supplied to the engine,
75 J are transformed into **kinetic energy** in the moving car,
5 J are wasted as **sound energy** and the rest is turned into **heat energy**.

On the graph paper below, draw an **energy transformation diagram** to illustrate Professor Bean's results. (You can use the graph paper 'sideways on' if you want.)

Top Tips: After you've finished drawing a fancy-smancy Sankey diagram it's a good idea to check that the input energy equals the total output energy (the useful energy **plus** the wasted energy). The number of input squares should balance with the total number of output arrow squares.

The Cost of Electricity

Q1 Match up the quantities used for calculating electricity costs with the correct units.

The **power** of an electrical appliance.

The **time** an appliance is used for.

The **price** of electrical energy.

The **electrical energy** used by an appliance.

Pence per kilowatt-hour

Kilowatt-hour (kWh)

Hour (h)

Kilowatt (kW)

Q2 All the units in the list below are units of **energy**, except for one.

kilojoule **kilowatt** **kilowatt-hour** **kWh** **J**

a) Circle the 'odd one out'.

b) What **is** this a unit of? ....

Q3 a) How many...

i) watts are there in one kilowatt? ....

ii) seconds are there in one hour? ....

iii) joules are there in one kilowatt-hour? ....

....

You'll have to use Energy = Power × Time

b) There is a mistake in each of the following statements. Write out a correct version underneath each one.

i) "**Unit**" is another name for "**kilowatt**."

....

ii) A domestic electricity meter measures **electrical energy** in **joules**.

....

....

The Cost of Electricity

Q4 The following statements are all incorrect. Write a correct version of each.

a) Power = energy × time.

....

b) 3 600 000 joules = 3.6 kJ

....

c) 1 kWh = 3 600 joules

....

d) 60 watts = 0.6 kilowatts

....

Q5 a) Calculate how many **kilowatt-hours** of electrical energy a **2 kW** electric heater uses in 3 hours.

Energy used (kWh)	=	power (kW)	×	time taken (hours)
	=	....	×	....
	=	.... kWh		

b) Boris gets his electricity supply from Ivasparkco. They charge 7 pence per kilowatt-hour. Work out the cost of the energy calculated in part (a)

Cost of energy	=	price of one kWh	×	number of kWh
	=	....	×	....
	=	.... pence		

Top Tips: Eeek — there's a horrible lot of units here. Make sure you've got it sussed that kilowatts are units of power, but kilowatt-hours are units of energy. Also, remember that kilo means 1000, so a kilowatt is 1000 watts and a kilometre is 1000 metres. Mega as in MJ means 1 000 000.

Energy Efficiency in the Home

Q1 Your home will be more **energy efficient** if you **reduce** the amount of heat **getting out** of it.

List four ways of keeping heat in your house.

1) ....

2) ....

3) ....

4) ....

Q2 Tick the correct boxes to show whether these statements are true or false.

		True	False
a)	Thermostatic controls make you more comfortable but don't save money.	☐	☐
b)	Fitting a jacket on a hot water tank is a fairly cheap way to save energy.	☐	☐
c)	Draught-proofing reduces heat losses because it reduces convection.	☐	☐

Q3 Draw arrows to match up the words with their meanings.

Cost	How much energy you save.
Cost-effectiveness	How much you have to pay.
Payback time	How long it takes to save as much as you spent initially.
Effectiveness	How worthwhile it is to spend the money.

Q4 Explain how the following types of insulation work.

a) Cavity wall insulation ....

....

b) Loft Insulation ....

....

c) Hot water tank jacket ....

....

Energy Efficiency in the Home

Q5 Heat is lost from a house through its **roof**, **walls**, **doors** and **windows**.

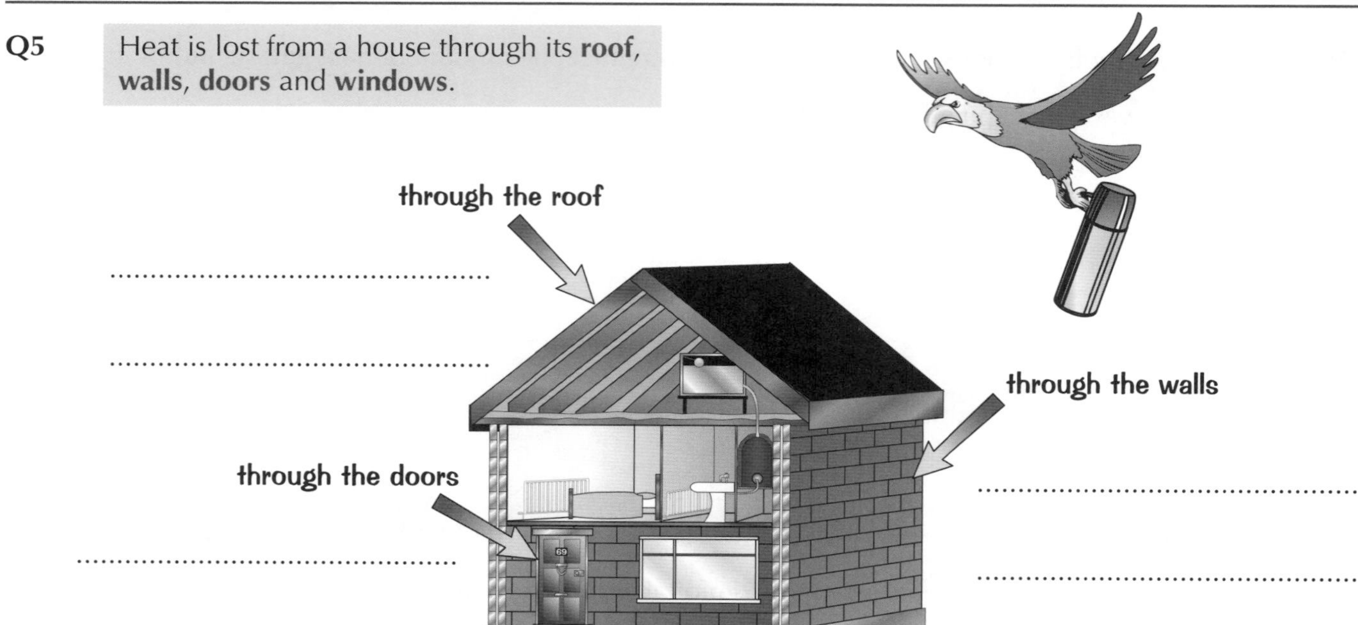

a) In the spaces on the diagram, write down at least one measure that could be taken to reduce heat losses through the roof, walls and doors.

b) Miss Jones has just bought a new house which has very large windows. Suggest three ways she could reduce heat loss through the windows of her new house.

1) ....

2) ....

3) ....

Q6 Mr Smith wants to buy **double glazing** for his house, but the salesman tries to sell him insulated window shutters instead. He says it is cheaper and more **cost-effective**.

	Double glazing	Insulated window shutters
Initial Cost	£3000	£1200
Annual Saving	£60	£20
Payback time	50 years	

a) Calculate the **payback time** for insulated shutters and write it in the table.

b) Is the salesman's advice correct? Give reasons for your answer.

....

....

Electricity and the National Grid

Q1 Number these statements 1 to 5 to show the order of the steps that are needed to deliver energy to Mrs Miggins' house so that she can boil the kettle.

	An electrical current flows through power cables across the country.
	Mrs Miggins boils the kettle for tea.
1	Electrical energy is generated in power stations.
	The voltage of the supply is raised.
	The voltage of the supply is reduced.

Q2 a) True or false?

	True	False
i) Houses always get electricity from their nearest power station.	☐	☐
ii) The National Grid carries electricity at 400 000 V.	☐	☐
iii) Power stations produce electricity at 400 000 V.	☐	☐
iv) Homes use electricity at 400 000 V.	☐	☐

b) Write a correction for each false sentence.

....

....

....

Q3 Using **high voltages** in power cables means you need some **expensive** equipment.

a) Make a list of the main equipment you need for **high voltage transmission**.

....

....

b) Explain why it is still **cheaper** to use **high voltages** for transmission.

....

....

Top Tips: The best tip I can give you about pylons is that if you're ever stuck on one, say because your parachute gets caught, and a friendly person comes along and offers you a metal ladder to get down, then DON'T use it. As soon as you touch the ladder, the electricity will go through you to the ground and you'll be instantly fried. You'll be fine as long as you don't touch anything else until the power is switched off. But your best bet by far is to not parachute anywhere near pylons.

Electricity and the National Grid

Q4 Mr Grimes is demonstrating a model of the National Grid to his pupils.

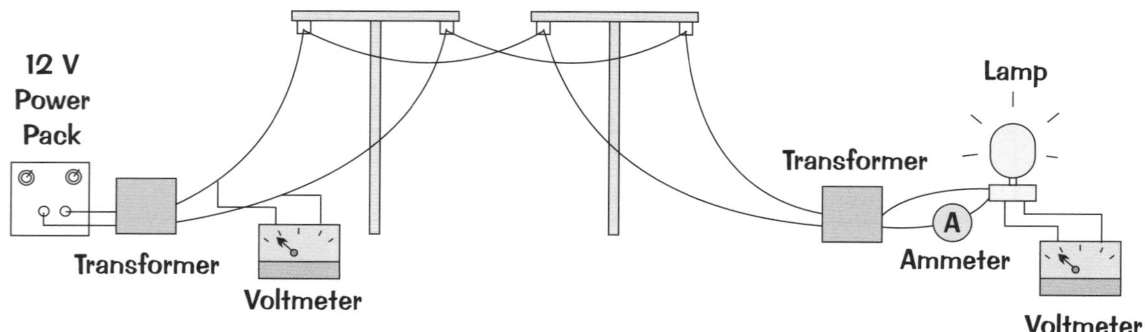

Mr Grimes measures the energy input and output at different **voltages**.
Here are his results.

Energy Input from power pack per second (J)	Voltage in cables (V)	Energy Output to lamp per second (J)	Brightness of lamp
18	24	18	very bright
18	18	17.9	bright
18	12	17.7	quite bright
18	6	17.0	fairly bright
18	4	15.2	not very bright

a) **i)** What is the dependent variable? ....

ii) What is the independent variable? ....

b) Why did Mr Grimes use the **same energy input** every time?

....

c) **i)** What happens to the **energy output** as the voltage is increased?

....

ii) Why does this happen?

....

....

Think about the energy transformations that take place in the cables.

Non-renewable Energy & Power Stations

Q1 Circle the correct words to complete these sentences.

a) Energy resources that will run out one day are called **renewable / non-renewable** resources.

b) We get most of our energy from **renewable / non-renewable** resources.

Q2 Write down the names of:

a) three fossil fuels. ...., ... and ....

b) a non-renewable energy source that is not a fossil fuel. ....

c) two gases that are released into the air when fossil fuels burn.

.... and ....

Q3 Most of our electricity is made in large power stations. There are several steps involved in this process. Number these steps in the right order.

- ☐ Hot steam rushes through a turbine and makes it spin.
- ☐ Electricity is produced by the spinning generator.
- ☐ A fossil fuel such as coal is burned to release heat.
- ☐ The spinning turbine makes the generator spin too.
- ☐ Water is heated in a boiler and turned to steam.

Q4 Match up each environmental problem below with something that causes it. Some problems may have the same cause.

Acid rain	Releasing CO_2 by burning fossil fuels
Rising CO_2 levels in the atmosphere	Using nuclear power
Climate change	Sulfur dioxide formed by burning oil and coal
Dangerous radioactive waste	Coal mining
Spoiling of natural landscapes	

Q5 Lisa says: "Using nuclear power to make electricity is too dangerous."
Tim says: "Using fossil fuels is even more dangerous in the long run."

Who do you think is right? Explain your answer.

....

....

Using Renewable Energy Resources (1)

Q1 Each of these statements is **false**.
Write out a correct version of each.

a) "Renewable" means "you can use it again".

....

b) Using renewable energy resources never damages the environment.

....

c) Renewable energy sources are all unreliable.

....

Q2 Circle the correct words to complete the sentences below.

Solar cells are used to **make electricity** / **heat water**. Once installed, they are a **cheap** / **expensive** way to generate electricity. Solar cells would be a good choice in **cloudy** / **remote** places.

Q3 Replacing a coal-fired power station with wind turbines could cause some problems.

Write down three objections there might be from people living near a proposed wind farm.

1. ....

2. ....

3. ....

Q4 Geoff wanted to find out how much electricity he could generate using a small wind turbine. Each night he used a wind-powered generator to charge a battery. On each following day, he timed how long the battery could keep a lamp lit. His results are shown in the table below.

Day	**Mon**	**Tues**	**Wed**	**Thu**	**Fri**	**Sat**	**Sun**
Time lamp stays lit (mins)	45	50	2	25	60	35	42

a) Why did Geoff time how long the lamp stayed lit?

....

b) Suggest a reason why the lamp only stayed lit for 2 minutes on Wednesday.

....

Using Renewable Energy Resources (2)

Q1 Complete the following passage using the words given below.

renewable turbines electricity generators dam

In a hydroelectric power station, water flows through ....
which drive .... which generate ....
New hydroelectric power stations can be expensive, because usually a
.... has to be built. However,
hydroelectric power is a .... source of energy.

Q2 State two possible environmental problems caused by using hydroelectric power.

1. ....

2. ....

Q3 'Pumped storage stations' and 'hydroelectric power stations' are different things.
Write the following phrases in the correct columns of the table to describe the difference.
Some phrases may go in both columns.

Has a turbine · Only needs one reservoir · Makes 'new' electricity · Needs two reservoirs · Must have a pump · Stores energy

Hydroelectric Power Station	Pumped Storage Station

Q4 These sentences explain how pumped storage works.
Put them in the right order by numbering them 1 to 4.

☐ Water at a high level stores energy until it is needed.

☐ At peak times water is allowed to flow downhill, powering turbines and generating electricity.

☐ At night big power stations make more electricity than is needed.

☐ Spare electricity is used to pump water from reservoirs at a low level to others at a high level.

Using Renewable Energy Resources (3)

Q1 Indicate whether the following statements are true or false.

		True	False
a)	Wave power generates most energy when the wind is strong.	☐	☐
b)	Wave power and tidal power both need turbines to generate electricity.	☐	☐
c)	Tidal power generates most electricity when the wind is strong.	☐	☐
d)	Tides happen because of the gravitational pull of the Moon and Sun.	☐	☐

Q2 **Wave-powered generators** can be very useful around islands, like Britain.

Number these sentences 1 to 6, to explain how a wave-powered generator works.

☐ The spinning generator makes electricity.
☐ The moving air makes the turbine spin.
☐ The water goes down again.
☐ Air is sucked downwards, spinning the turbine the other way and generating more power.
☐ A wave moves water upwards, forcing air out towards a turbine.
☐ The spinning turbine drives a generator.

Q3 Explain how a **tidal barrage** generates electricity.

....

....

....

Q4 Tidal power and wave power both have some disadvantages.

a) Write down two problems with using wave power.

1. ....

2. ....

b) Write down two problems with using tidal power.

1. ....

2. ....

Using Renewable Energy Resources (3)

Q5 Glenn lives by the sea. During his summer holidays, he investigates the local tides and waves.

He recorded the difference in sea level between high tide and low tide on several days in August, using a tidal gauge. He also estimated the average height of the waves.

Date	01/08	03/08	07/08	10/08	13/08	16/08	19/08	22/08	25/08	28/08
Difference between high tide and low tide (m)	10.5	10.0	4.6	4.8	7.7	8.4	7.5	5.2	4.9	9.3
Height of waves (m)	0.2	0.5	0.2	1.5	0.4	0.2	0.6	1.6	1.1	0.8

a) On which date could you get most energy from:

i) Tidal power? ....

ii) Wave power? ....

b) What should Glenn have done to make his estimate of **average wave height** as reliable as possible?

Strong winds mean big waves, and wind strength might change during the day.

....

....

c) In Glenn's results, which varied more — the difference between high and low tide, or the average height of the waves? Explain your answer.

....

....

d) An electricity generating company wants to build a tidal barrage near Glenn's house. They send out a leaflet which states that "Tidal power is more reliable than wave power."

i) Do Glenn's results support this claim? Explain your answer.

....

....

ii) Why might Glenn object to a tidal barrage being built near his house?

....

....

Top Tips: What did the fish say when he swam into a wall? Dam.

Using Renewable Energy Resources (4)

Q1 Number these sentences 1 to 5 to describe the process of generating electricity from geothermal energy.

- [ ] The water is heated and turns to steam.
- [ ] Water is pumped down to the hot rocks.
- [ ] A generator driven by the turbine makes electricity.
- [ ] Deep holes are drilled down into hot rocks.
- [ ] Steam comes up to the surface and powers a turbine.

Q2 Indicate whether these statements are true or false.

		True	False
a)	Burning biomass does not release CO_2 into the atmosphere.	☐	☐
b)	Burning landfill rubbish does not cause pollution.	☐	☐
c)	Some biomass is turned into other fuels before it is burnt.	☐	☐
d)	Plants are sometimes grown specifically to be burnt as biomass.	☐	☐

Q3 Explain why:

a) Some rocks underground are very hot.

....

b) Biomass is a 'renewable' source of energy.

....

c) Burning biomass is 'carbon neutral'.

....

Q4 Mr Saleem is a cattle farmer in India. He lives 40 miles from the nearest large town. Mr Saleem has just installed a small **biogas** plant on his farm. He uses the gas for cooking and heating.

a) What source of biogas is Mr Saleem likely to use?

....

b) Apart from cooking and heating, how else could Mr Saleem make use of the biogas?

....

Comparison of Energy Resources

Q1 Many old coal- and oil-fired power stations are being taken out of use.

a) Suggest one reason for this.

....

b) State three reasons why gas-fired power stations are often chosen to replace old coal-fired and oil-fired power stations.

1) ....

2) ....

3) ....

Q2 Five different locations are shown in the diagram below.
Label each diagram with the type of power station which would be most suitable.

Tidal Wind Wave Hydroelectric

....

....

Q3 Plans to build new hydroelectric power stations can be controversial.

a) Explain why it takes a **long time** and is **expensive** to build large hydroelectric power stations.

....

....

b) Suggest two environmental issues which might make people object to the plans.

1) ....

2) ....

Comparison of Energy Resources

Q4 The city of Fakeville decides to replace its old coal-fired power station. They have to choose between using gas, nuclear, wind or biomass.

Give one **disadvantage** of each choice:

a) **Gas** ....

....

b) **Nuclear** ....

....

c) **Wind** ....

....

d) **Biomass** ....

....

Q5 This is part of a leaflet produced by the pressure group 'Nuclear Is Not the Answer' (NINA).

Read the extract and answer the questions on the next page.

> Imagine life without electricity. No lights, no computers, no TV… no kettles, no tea? Unthinkable. But that's what could happen when the oil and gas run out — because in the UK we generate about 80% of our electricity from power stations running on fossil fuels.
>
> The Government is considering whether we should build more nuclear power stations. At NINA, we believe that nuclear is not the answer.
>
> Nuclear power stations generate power, yes, but they also generate huge piles of highly radioactive waste. No one has any idea how to get rid of this waste safely. So should we really be making more of it? Radioactive waste stays dangerous for hundreds of thousands of years. Would you be happy living near a nuclear fuel dump? That's not all — nuclear power stations, and the lethal waste they create, are obvious targets for terrorists. And, last but not least, building more nuclear power stations would cost the taxpayer billions.
>
> The good news is, we don't need nuclear power. There are safer, cleaner ways to produce electricity — using renewable energy. Many people argue that renewables are unreliable — the wind doesn't always blow, for instance. Well, true, but tidal power is reliable — and we have hundreds of miles of coastline with tides washing in and out twice every day.
>
> There's still time. If you don't want your children to grow up in a nuclear-powered world, join NINA today.

Comparison of Energy Resources

a) The authors of the leaflet ask us to imagine what life might be like without electricity.

i) Why do they think we might not have any electricity?

....

ii) What do they say the Government is thinking of doing about this?

....

b) The leaflet argues that nuclear power "is not the answer".

i) According to the leaflet, what is the main problem with nuclear power?
Circle the correct answer.

A it's unreliable **B** it produces dangerous waste **C** it's expensive **D** it's non-renewable

ii) How does the leaflet suggest we can avoid the problem?

....

....

c) Do you think the leaflet presents a **balanced** view, or is it **biased**?
Explain your answer.

I think the leaflet presents a **balanced** / **biased** view, because ....

....

....

d) Write down one example from the text of:

i) A scientific argument against nuclear power ....

....

ii) A non-scientific argument against nuclear power ....

....

Top Tips: There's no perfect energy resource — they all have advantages and disadvantages. Which advantages outweigh which disadvantages is a matter of opinion — there's no right answer. In fact, we'll probably need to carry on getting our energy from many different sources — it's just that the mix might change, away from fossil fuels towards nuclear energy or renewables.

Mixed Questions — Physics 1a

Q1 Explain:

a) how a layer of **snow** can stop young plants dying in the **frost**.

....

....

b) why birds try to keep warm in winter by **ruffling** up their feathers.

....

....

c) why, in winter, **cloudy** nights are usually **warmer** than clear nights.

....

....

Q2 Ben sets up an experiment. He paints two identical pieces of metal with different coatings. He lights the Bunsen burner and records the temperature readings on thermometers A and B every two minutes.

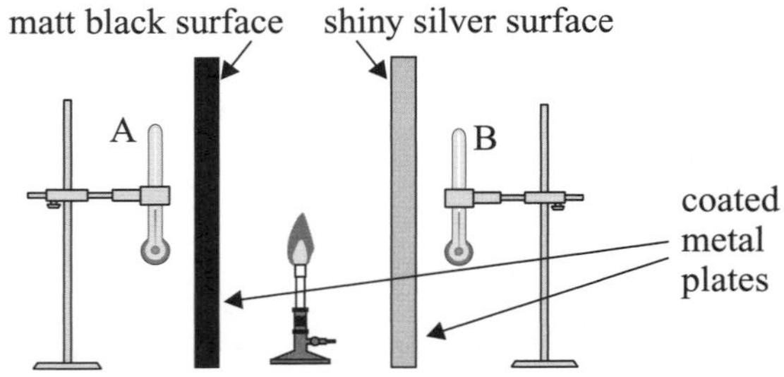

The graph below shows Ben's results for thermometer **B**.

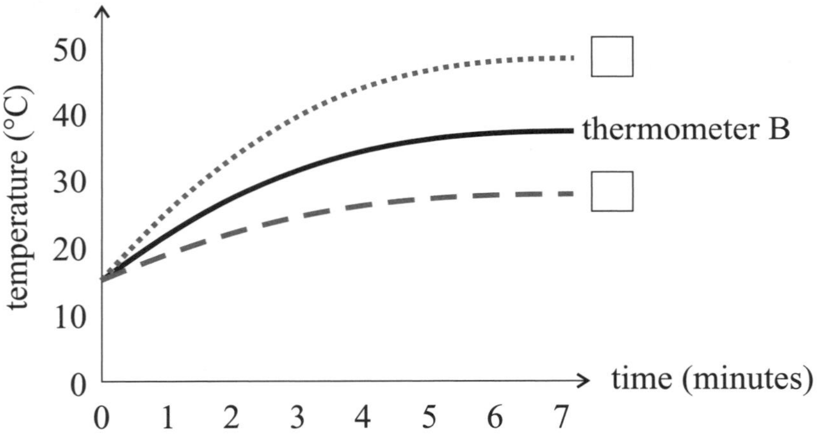

matt black surface
shiny silver surface
A
B
coated metal plates

temperature (°C)
50
40
30
20
10
0
0 1 2 3 4 5 6 7
time (minutes)
thermometer B

a) Which of the two dotted curves show the results you might expect for thermometer **A**? Tick the box next to the one you think is correct.

b) Which of the two coatings, A or B, would you choose to paint a **radiator**? Explain your answer.

Coating .... because ....

....

Mixed Questions — Physics 1a

Q3 Jemima is sanding some floorboards with an **electric sander** which has a power rating of **500 W**. Jemima has the sander on for **30 minutes**.

a) **i)** How many kilowatt-hours of electrical energy does the sander use in this time?

....

ii) How many **joules** of energy is this?

....

b) The sander is only **60% efficient**. How many **joules** of energy are **wasted**?

....

c) Jemima's electricity supplier charges **10p per Unit** (a Unit is 1 kilowatt-hour).

i) For £1, how many Units could Jemima use?

....

ii) Use your answer to part i) and the equation given here to calculate how long Jemima can use the sander for, for a cost of £1.
Give your answer in hours and minutes.

$$\text{Time} = \frac{\text{Units}}{\text{Power}}$$

....

....

Q4 A group of farmers live on a remote Scottish island. The island is quite mountainous and the weather is often cloudy and/or rainy. The islanders decide to put up **wind turbines** to generate **electricity**.

a) Most of the UK's electricity is generated in **fossil fuel** fired power stations. Suggest why the islanders **don't** want to rely on these power stations.

....

b) **i)** Why might they have chosen to use **wind power** to generate electricity?

....

ii) Sometimes, the wind doesn't blow and the wind turbines won't generate electricity. Suggest a way the islanders could **store** energy for use when there is no wind.

....

c) **i)** Suggest one other **renewable energy source** you might advise the islanders to consider.

....

ii) Give one reason the islanders might choose **not** to use this source.

....

Mixed Questions — Physics 1a

Q5 Eric investigates ways of saving energy in his grandmother Ethel's house. He calculates the annual savings that could be made on Ethel's fuel bills, and the cost of doing the work.

Work needed	Annual Saving (£)	Cost of work (£)
Hot water tank jacket	15	15
Draught-proofing	65	70
Cavity wall insulation	70	560
Thermostatic controls	25	120

a) Cavity wall insulation is the most expensive to install of the measures that Eric has investigated, but it also gives the highest annual savings.

i) Calculate the **payback time** for cavity wall insulation. ....

ii) Ethel thinks she might move house in the next two years. Do you think she should install cavity wall insulation? Circle **should** or **should not** and explain your answer.

I think she **should** / **should not** install cavity wall insulation because ....

....

iii) Which of the options in the table would save Ethel the most money **over two years**? Show all your working.

....

....

....

b) In Ethel's living room, there is an open fire which burns logs.

i) Is **wood** a renewable or non-renewable source of energy? Explain your answer.

....

ii) Fill in the missing words to describe the main energy transfers when the fire is burning.

.... **energy →** .... **energy + light energy**

c) Ethel's hot water is heated by an immersion heater in the hot water tank. This has an electric **element** which heats the water immediately surrounding it.

Eventually, almost all the water in the tank also gets hot, even though it is not next to the element. Explain how this happens.

heating element

....

....

Mixed Questions — Physics 1a

Q6 In one gas-fired power station, for every **1000 J** of energy input to the power station, 100 J is wasted in the **boiler**, 500 J is wasted in the **cooling water** and 50 J is wasted in the **generator**.

a) For each 1000 J of energy input, how much useful energy **output** does the power station produce?

....

b) Calculate the **efficiency** of the power station.

....

c) On the grid below, draw a detailed energy transformation diagram for this power station.

d) Electricity generated in power stations reaches our homes by a network of power cables. Explain:

i) why these power cables are at very high voltages

....

....

ii) why the high voltage of the cables is not dangerous for people using electricity in their houses

....

....

Electromagnetic Waves

Q1 Complete the following sentences by choosing the correct words from those given below.

light matter energy sound

All electromagnetic waves transfer .... from place to place.

In a vacuum they travel at the speed of ....

Q2 Diagrams A, B and C represent electromagnetic waves.

A B C

a) Which two diagrams show waves with the same **frequency**? .... and ....

b) Which two diagrams show waves with the same **amplitude**? .... and ....

c) Which two diagrams show waves with the same **wavelength**? .... and ....

Q3 Ultraviolet waves, microwaves and gamma waves are all types of electromagnetic wave.

Write them out in order of **wavelength**, shortest first.

....

Q4 Indicate whether the following statements are true or false.

		True	False
a)	In a vacuum, visible light travels faster than both X-rays and radio waves.	☐	☐
b)	X-rays have higher frequency than visible light and infrared.	☐	☐
c)	Radio waves have the shortest wavelength of all EM waves.	☐	☐
d)	All EM waves can travel through a vacuum.	☐	☐

Q5 A radio wave travels at 3×10^8 m/s and has a frequency of 300 000 Hz. Calculate its **wavelength**.

You're given the speed (v) and frequency (f). You'll have to rearrange $v = f\lambda$ to find wavelength (λ).

....

....

....

Electromagnetic Waves

Q6 Many people have a satellite dish on their house to receive TV signals.

Fill in the missing words from the list below to describe how this works.

reflects	absorbs	frequency	alternating current

The satellite dish .... electromagnetic waves onto a centrally positioned aerial. This .... the waves and changes them into an .... (with the same .... as the electromagnetic waves). This signal is then sent to the TV set.

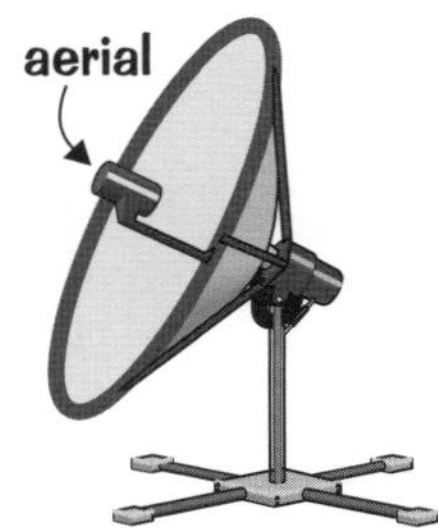

Q7 High doses of **UV** radiation can cause cancer. **Radio** waves are very unlikely to damage humans.

Explain why these two types of electromagnetic wave have such different effects.

....

....

....

Q8 The diagram shows equipment used to test how well materials absorb electromagnetic radiation. If **all** of the radiation reaches the detector it reads **10**, and if **none** of it passes through, it reads **0**.

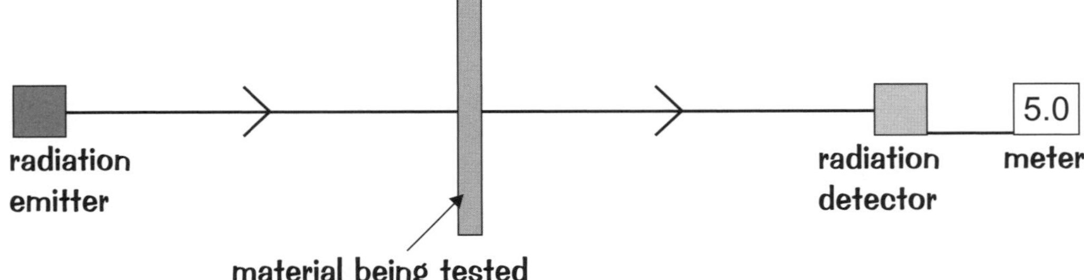

a) The material being tested gave a reading of 5, so half the energy passed through. What **two things** may have happened to the rest of the energy when it hit this material?

....

b) Another, much **thicker** sample of the **same material** is tested. How do you expect the reading on the detector to change, if at all? Explain your answer.

....

....

Electromagnetic Waves

Q9 The house shown below receives radio signals from a nearby transmitter, even though there is a mountain between the house and the transmitter.

Use the words below to fill in the blanks in the passage.

ionosphere **short-wave** **long-wave** **alternating current** **absorbs**

The house can receive .... signals because they can bend around the mountain. It also receives .... signals because they are reflected by the .... A radio has an aerial which .... the EM waves and changes them into an ....

Q10 The diagrams show the arrangement of atoms in a dense material and in a less dense material.

dense material **less dense material**

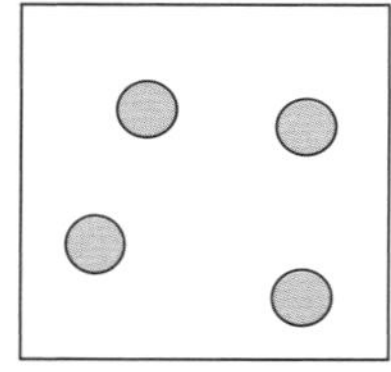

Dense materials are more likely to **reflect** or **absorb** electromagnetic waves. **Less dense** materials are more likely to transmit them.

Explain why this is.

Try drawing a ray of light hitting the material. How likely is it to hit an atom (and what happens to its energy when it does?)

....

....

....

Top Tips: **Absorption** of EM radiation can cause **heating** (useful in ovens) and/or an **alternating current** (useful in radios etc.). Radiation isn't always absorbed though — it could be reflected or transmitted. This depends on **what** the material is, and the **wavelength** of the radiation.

Microwaves and Infrared

Q1 Ellie, in Britain, is talking to her Canadian friend Brad by mobile phone.

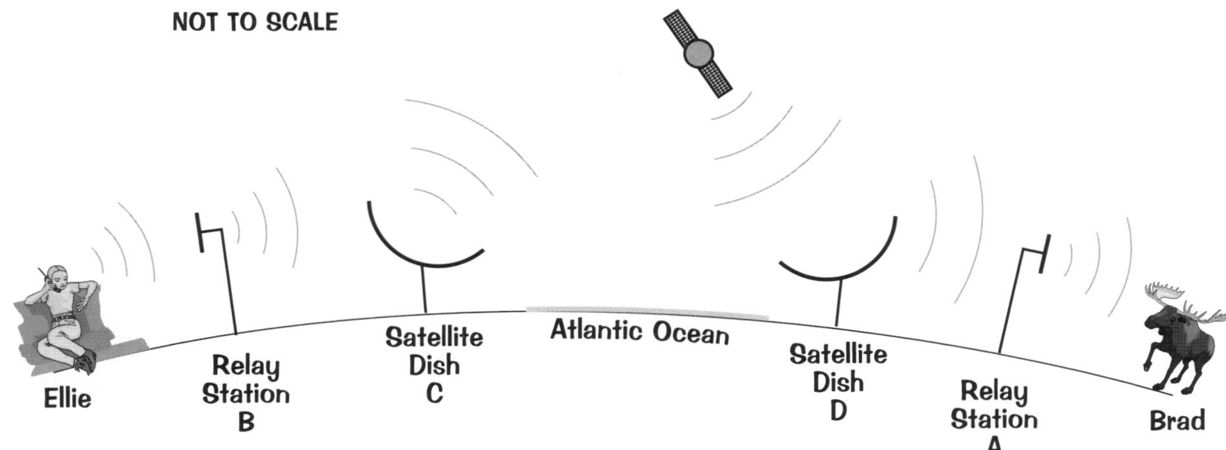

Use the letters and words below to complete the passage.

A B C D microwave sound transmitted absorbed

Ellie's phone emits microwave energy which is .... at Relay Station .... and then .... to Satellite Dish C. This dish transmits the signal to a satellite orbiting in space, which boosts the signal and sends it to Satellite Dish .... in Canada. The signal reaches Brad's phone via Relay Station .... His phone then changes the .... energy into .... energy.

Q2 The diagram shows two ways you can receive TV signals — from a satellite dish on your house, or from a cable company with a much larger satellite dish.

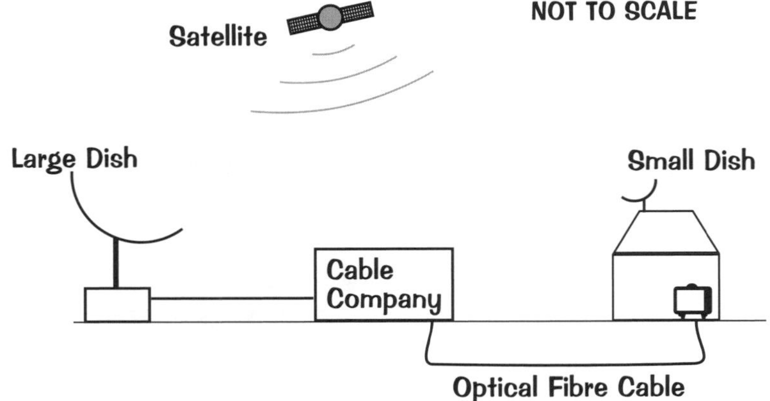

Indicate whether the following statements are **true** or **false** (write T or F as appropriate).

a) The small and the large dish receive the same signals from the satellite. .....

b) The optical fibre cable uses microwaves to send signals to your TV. .....

c) Signals sent by optical fibre are less likely to suffer from electrical interference than signals sent along copper wires. .....

d) The signal in the cable will need boosting when travelling long distances. .....

Microwaves and Infrared

Q3 a) The diagrams show rays of light in an **optical fibre**.

Draw arrows to match each diagram to the correct description of what is happening.

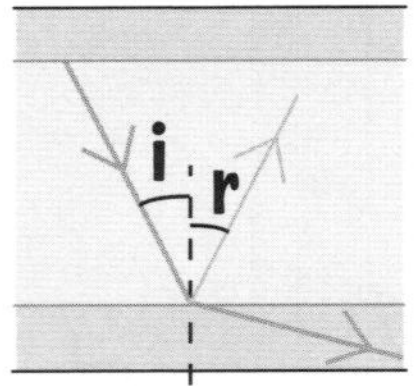

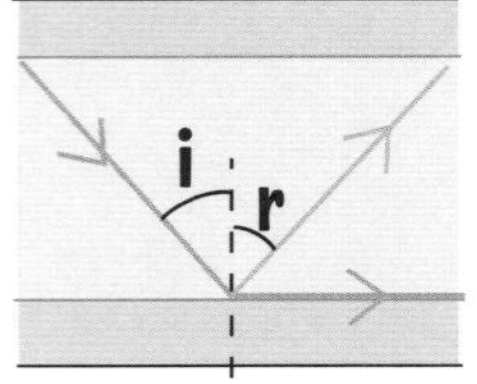

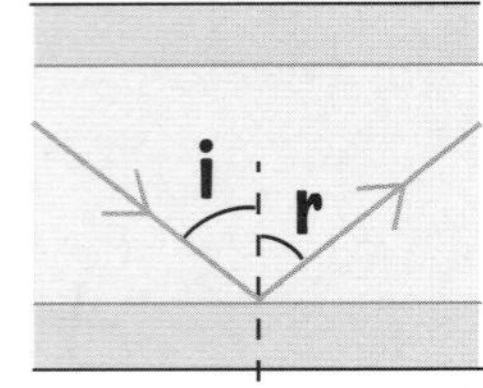

Total internal reflection

Most of the light passes out of the optical fibre, but some is reflected internally.

Most of the light is reflected internally, but some emerges along the surface of the glass.

b) The critical angle for glass/air is 42°. Using this fact, complete the ray diagrams below.

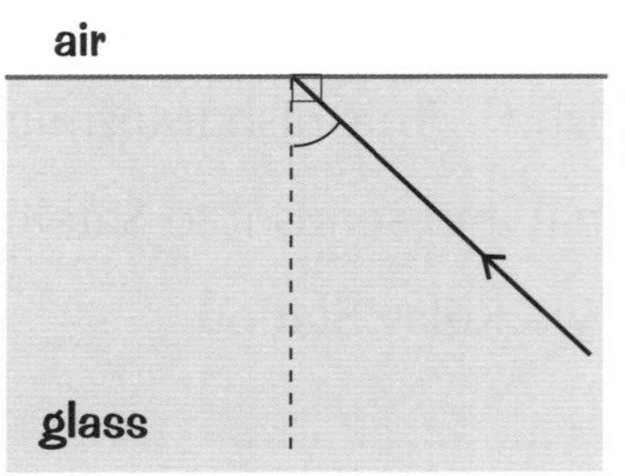

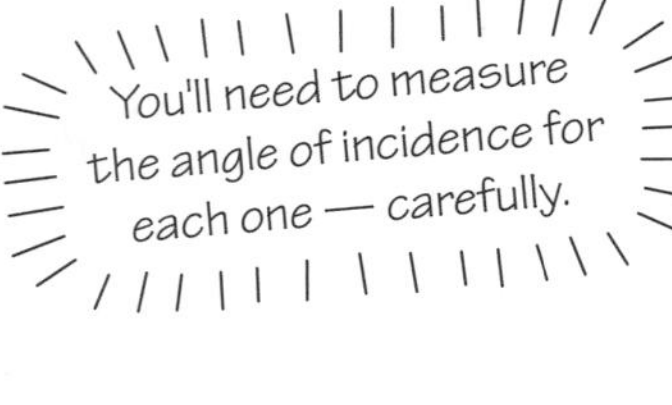

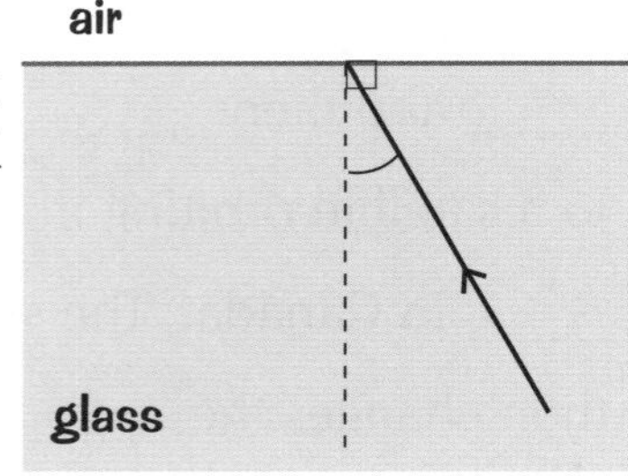

c) Explain why it is important not to **bend** an optical fibre sharply.

....

....

Q4 Microwaves are used for **cooking** as well as for mobile phone **communications**.

Explain why your body does not get 'cooked' when you use a mobile phone.

....

....

Q5 Explain how a microwave camera on a remote-sensing satellite can 'see' through clouds.

....

....

Microwaves and Infrared

Q6 Read this extract about the safety of microwave ovens.

> Microwave ovens are designed to generate microwaves to heat up food. So should we be worried that microwaves are cooking us, as well as our dinner?
>
> Well, probably not. The Microwave Technologies Association, which represents manufacturers, stresses that microwave ovens are lined with metal to stop microwaves getting out, and that there are regulations about how much 'leakage' is allowed. They also point out that the leakage decreases rapidly with distance from the oven. So don't press your nose to the glass to watch your chicken korma reheating — gaze from a distance.
>
> We can't be certain that microwave ovens are absolutely safe — there might be long-term health problems that no one's spotted yet. But perhaps we should be more worried about other uses of microwave technology, like mobile phones. Mobile phones use microwaves — though of a lower frequency than those used in ovens. But mobile phones are very definitely *designed* to emit microwaves (or else they wouldn't work) — so are they silently 'cooking' our brains?
>
> Interestingly, my mobile phone can still make calls from inside a microwave oven, with the door shut. If the microwaves from my phone are powerful enough to get out of the oven — with all its fancy shielding — then what on earth are they doing to my brain?

a) Why might it be a serious health hazard if microwaves 'leak' from microwave ovens?

....

....

b) According to the article, microwave ovens have a **metal lining** to stop microwaves getting out. This suggests that microwaves may be (circle any which apply):

A absorbed by the metal lining

B reflected by the metal lining

C transmitted by the metal lining

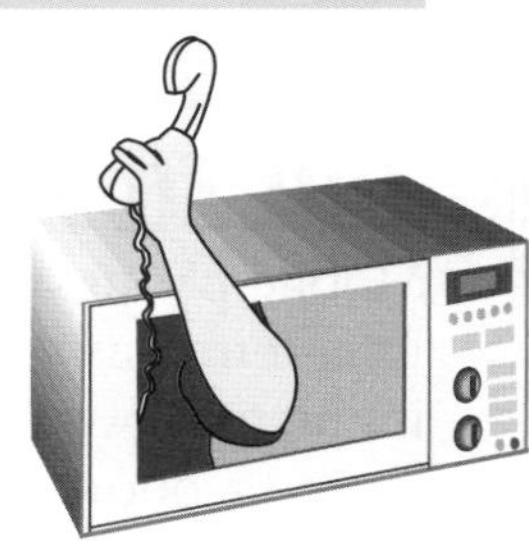

Microwaves and Infrared

c) Why does the article advise you not to "press your nose to the glass" of a microwave oven? Circle the correct answer.

A because the radiation from microwave ovens is known to cause cancer

B because some radiation may be "leaking" from the oven

C to avoid bruising

D because you might burn your skin

d) Why does keeping your distance from a microwave oven reduce the chance that you will suffer harmful effects from it?

....

....

e) Why does the article mention that the Microwave Technologies Association represents manufacturers?

....

....

f) Mobile phones also emit microwaves when you are making a call.

i) Do the microwaves emitted by **mobile phones** have a longer or shorter **wavelength** than those used in ovens? Circle the correct answer.

longer **shorter**

ii) Why does the author suggest that we should be more concerned about the ill effects of microwaves from mobile phones than from microwave ovens?

....

....

Top Tips: People love a good scare story. Microwave ovens are **probably** perfectly safe. Mobile phones haven't been around for so long, so it's difficult to know if they're doing us any long-term harm. But I know people who would say it's safer to stay at home, heating up ready meals in the microwave and making calls on your mobile, than it is to cross a busy, fume-choked city street to find a phone box or go to the pizza shop. Watch out for the salt in those ready meals, though.

Hazards of EM Radiation

Q1 Describe the link between the **frequency** of electromagnetic waves and how **dangerous** they are.

....

Q2 The diagram shows an enlargement of part of the door of a microwave oven.

Black paint

'Holes' in the paint, 2 mm in diameter.

Microwaves have a wavelength of about 12 cm and cannot pass through the 'holes' in the black paint. Visible light can pass through the holes so you can see inside the oven.

Explain why **light can** pass through the 'holes', but **microwaves can't**.

Compare the wavelengths of light and microwaves.

....

....

Q3 Indicate whether the following statements are **true** (write **T**) or **false** (write **F**).

a) Darker skinned people are less likely to suffer from skin cancer. ....

b) UV light can damage the DNA in the cells of our skin. ....

c) Suncream with SPF 5 is better at protecting you than SPF 15 cream. ....

d) Fluorescent light tubes emit significant amounts of harmful UV radiation. ....

e) Infrared and visible light are always safe. ....

Q4 Use the words below to complete this passage.

lead	reproductive organs	bone	soft tissue	absorbed

X-rays are useful for finding broken bones because they pass easily through .... but are .... more by .... Screens and shields made of .... are used to protect the radiographer and minimise the patient's exposure to X-rays, especially in vulnerable parts of the body like the ....

Analogue and Digital Signals

Q1 Tick the boxes to show whether these statements are true or false.

		True	False
a)	Analogue signals can be carried through space by an electromagnetic wave.	☐	☐
b)	Digital signals have to be sent along copper cables.	☐	☐
c)	Digital signals can be sent as light waves in optical fibres.	☐	☐

Q2 Devices X and Y both emit EM radiation.

a) Which device emits an analogue signal? ....

b) Which device emits a digital signal? ....

c) Which device sent a pulsed signal? ....

Signal from Device X

Signal from Device Y

Q3 Write 'A' or 'D' under each device below, to show whether it is **analogue** or **digital**.

Dimmer Switch

....

Q4 Fill in the blanks, using the words below.

analogue	amplified	weaken	interference	noise

All signals .... as they travel. To overcome this, they can be .... Signals can also suffer .... from other signals or from electrical disturbances. This causes .... in the signal. When .... signals are amplified, the noise is also amplified.

Q5 Modern communication systems often involve computers.

a) Explain why it is better to send a **digital** signal to a computer rather than an analogue one.

....

....

b) State two other advantages of using digital signals for communication.

....

....

Radioactivity

Q1 This is a diagram of an atom.

a) Write down which letter shows:

i) The nucleus ....

ii) Electrons ....

iii) Neutrons and protons ....

b) Complete the table below about the particles that are found in an atom.

Name of particle	Type of charge (positive/negative)	Where to find it (in nucleus/orbiting)
		Orbiting the nucleus
Proton		
	None	

Q2 Fill in the blanks using the words below. Each word should be used only once.

radiation **element** **protons** **neutrons** **nuclei** **radioactive**

Isotopes are atoms which have the same number of .... but different numbers of .... Some isotopes are .... Their .... are unstable, so they break down and spit out .... When this happens the nucleus often changes into a new ....

Q3 Carbon-14 is radioactive but carbon-12 is not. What is the difference between their **nuclei**?

....

....

Q4 Indicate whether these sentences are **true** or **false**.

		True	False
a)	The nucleus of an atom takes up almost no space compared to the whole atom.	☐	☐
b)	Most of an atom's mass is in the electrons.	☐	☐
c)	Atoms of the same element with the same number of neutrons are called isotopes.	☐	☐
d)	Radioactive decay speeds up at higher temperatures.	☐	☐

Radioactivity

Q5 What are the three types of nuclear radiation?

.... , ... , ...

Q6 a) Which sentence correctly explains what "ionising" radiation is? Circle the right answer.

A Ionising radiation is radiation that can penetrate many materials.

B Ionising radiation is radiation that can knock electrons off atoms.

C Ionising radiation is radiation that can do damage when it is stopped.

b) The three types of radiation — **α**, **β** and **γ** — could be compared to a **tank**, a **cannon ball** and a **laser beam** entering a forest.
Out of the tank, the cannon ball and the laser beam, which one

i) travels fastest? ....

ii) is likely to get furthest into the forest before hitting a tree? ....

c) Circle the correct words to complete these sentences.

i) When ionising radiation hits atoms, it can turn them into **isotopes** / **ions**.

ii) Strongly ionising radiations travel **further** / **less far** into a material.

iii) Strongly ionising radiations cause **more** / **less** damage in the materials they penetrate.

Q7 Complete the table below by choosing the correct word from each column.

Radiation Type	Ionising power weak/moderate/ strong	Charge positive/none/ negative	Relative mass no mass/ small/large	Penetrating power low/moderate/ high	Relative speed slow/fast/ very fast
alpha					
beta					
gamma					

Top Tips: You need to know how α, β and γ radiation are different. So make sure you've got that table right — and think about the patterns in ionising power, penetrating power, speed etc.

Radioactivity

Q8 a) For each sentence, tick the correct box to show whether it is **true** or **false**.

	True	False
i) All radiations are deflected by magnetic fields.	☐	☐
ii) Gamma radiation has no mass because it is an EM wave.	☐	☐
iii) Alpha is the slowest and most strongly ionising type of radiation.	☐	☐
iv) Beta particles are electrons, so they do not come from the nucleus.	☐	☐

b) For each of the false sentences, write out a correct version.

....

....

....

Q9 Radiation from three sources — A, B and C — was directed through an **electric field** (between X and Y), towards target sheets of **paper**, **aluminium** and **lead**.
Counters were used to detect where radiation passed through the target sheets.

Source A — the radiation was partially absorbed by the lead.
Source B — the radiation was deflected by the electric field, and stopped by the paper.
Source C — the radiation was deflected by the electric field, and stopped by the aluminium.

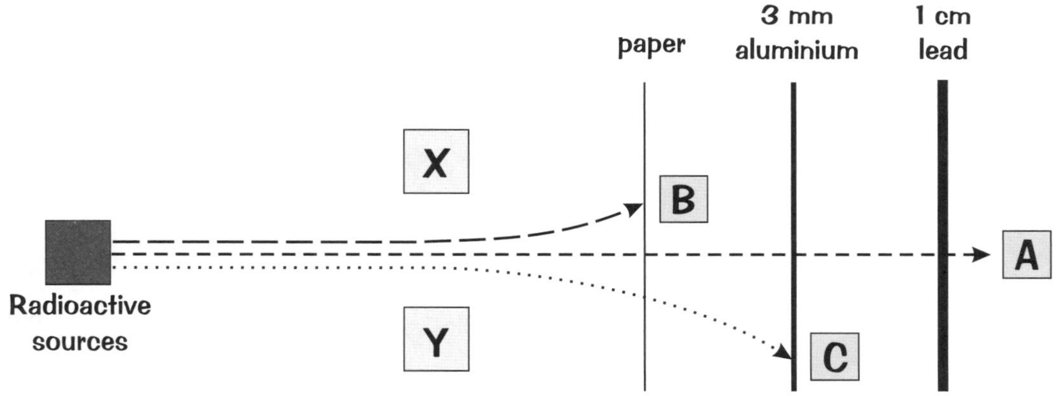

paper | 3 mm aluminium | 1 cm lead

X

Y

B

A

C

Radioactive sources

a) What type of radiation is emitted by:

source A? ...., source B? ...., source C? ....

b) Explain why radiation from source A is not deflected by the electric field.

....

....

c) What other type of **field** would deflect radiation from sources B and C? ....

Half-life

Q1 One of the statements below is **wrong**.
Circle the relevant letter and write a correct version underneath.

A The radioactivity of a source always decreases with time.

B Each time a radioactive nucleus decays, the activity of the source increases.

C The radioactivity decreases quickly for some materials but slowly for others.

....

Q2 The table below shows how the count rate of a radioactive source is expected to change with time.

Time (minutes)	1	2	3	4	5	6	7	8	9	10
Count Rate	1024	512	256							

a) Complete the table.

b) What is the **half-life** of this source? ....

Q3 The diagrams represent what happens to 100 nuclei in a substance with a half-life of **30 minutes**.

A — at the beginning

unstable nuclei

B — after one hour

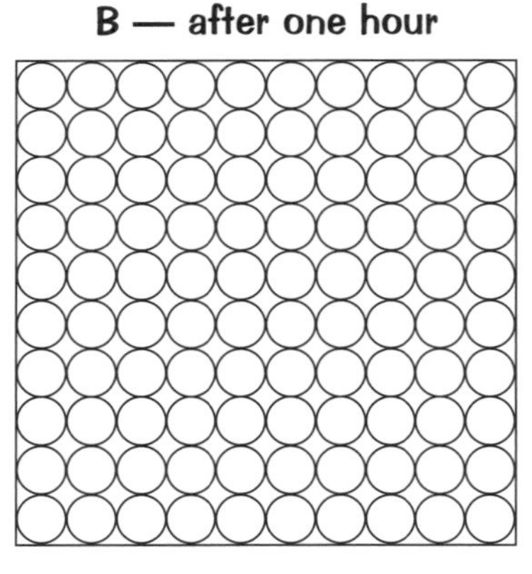

C — after how long?

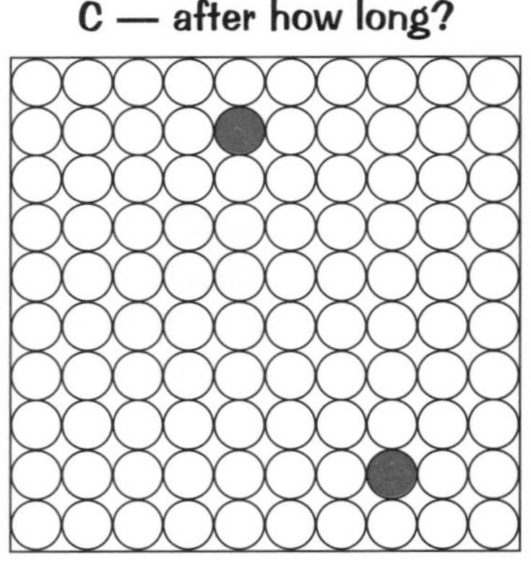

a) Complete diagram B to show the number of unstable nuclei you would expect after **one hour**.

b) Roughly how much time has passed in diagram C? ....

Top Tips: Half-life tells you **how quickly** a source becomes **less radioactive**. If your source has a half-life of 50 years then after 100 years the count rate will be 1/4 of its original value. But if the half-life's 10 years, after 100 years the count rate will be less than 1/1000th of its original value.

Half-life

Q4 A radioactive isotope has a half-life of 60 years.
Which statement describes this isotope correctly? Tick one box only.

- In 60 years half of the atoms in the material will have gone. ☐
- In 30 years' time only half the atoms will be radioactive. ☐
- In 60 years' time the count rate will be half what it is now. ☐
- In about 180 years there will be almost no radioactivity left in the material. ☐

Q5 The graph shows how the count rate of a radioactive isotope declines with time.

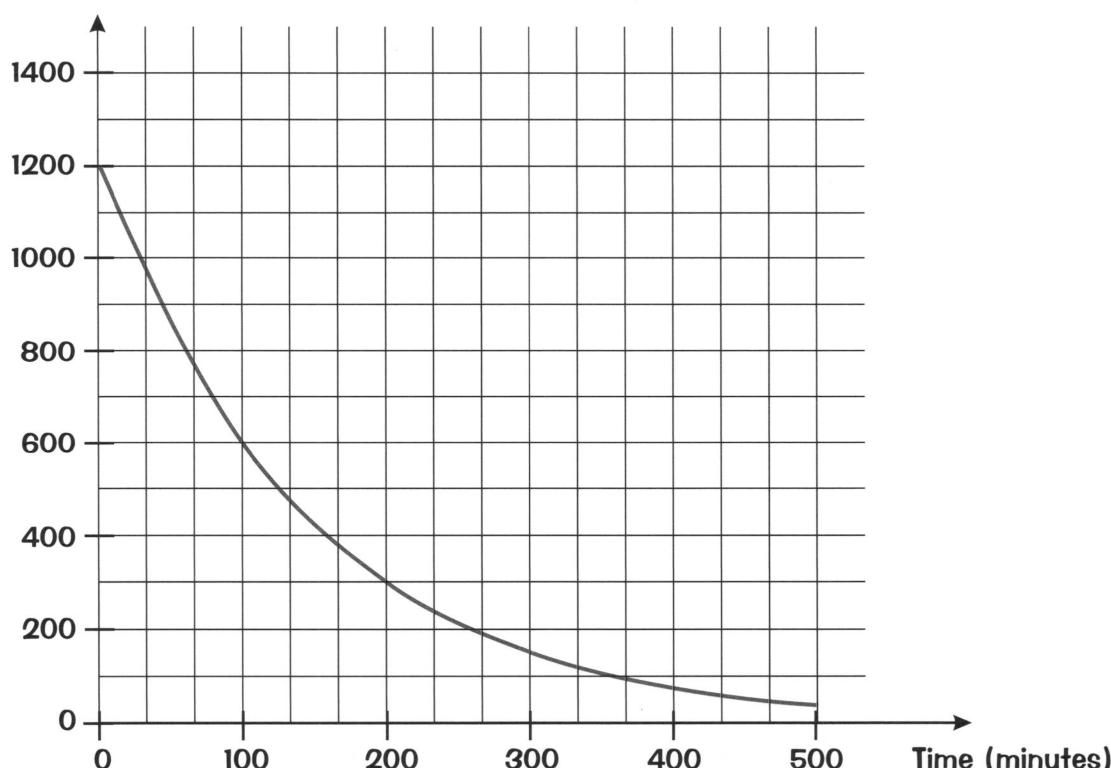

a) What is the half-life of this isotope? ....

b) What was the count rate after 3 half-lives? ....

c) What fraction of the original radioactive nuclei will still be unstable after 300 minutes?

....

d) After how long was the count rate down to 300 cpm? ....

Uses of Radiation

Q1 Indicate whether these statements, about **medical tracers**, are true or false.

		True	False
a)	Gamma radiation is never used in medical tracers because it is too penetrating.	☐	☐
b)	Alpha radiation is never used because it is too ionising.	☐	☐
c)	Radioactive sources with a long half-life are used so that their effects last longer.	☐	☐
d)	After a short time, the radioactivity of the tracer becomes very low.	☐	☐
e)	A detector is put inside the body to measure the radiation.	☐	☐

Q2 Materials that emit **gamma radiation** can be injected into underground pipes to find leaks.

a) Why does gamma radiation have to be used?

....

b) The radioactive source that is used should have a **short half-life**. Why?

....

Q3 The table shows the **properties** needed for different uses of radioactivity, and the **types** of radioactive sources that are used.

Choose the appropriate words to complete the table (some have been done for you).

Use of radiation	**Penetrating power** (low/high)	**Ionising power** (low/high)	**Half-life** (short/long)	**Type of radiation** (α,β,γ)
Smoke alarm	Low			
Medical tracers			Short	
Detecting leaks in pipes		Low		

Q4 The following sentences explain how a smoke detector works, but they are in the wrong order.

Put them in order — by labelling them 1 to 6.

- ☐ The circuit is broken so no current flows.
- 1 The radioactive source emits alpha particles.
- ☐ A current flows between the electrodes — the alarm stays off.
- ☐ The alarm sounds.
- ☐ The air between the electrodes is ionised by the alpha particles.
- ☐ A fire starts and smoke particles absorb the alpha radiation.

Bike Sheds

Risks from Radiation

Q1 **Three** of the following statements are **true**. Circle the appropriate letters.

A Both gamma and alpha radiation pass easily through the body.

B Alpha radiation damages cells in a very localised area of the body.

C Ionisation does not always kill cells — sometimes it causes them to mutate.

D Cancer occurs when a large number of cells are killed.

E The dose of radiation received depends on the length of exposure.

Q2 Read the following passage and fill in the blanks using the words given below.

tumour	**radiotherapy**	**high**	**dividing**	**gamma**

Cancers can sometimes be treated with .... rays.
A .... dose is used, directed towards the
.... This stops the cancer cells ....
This treatment is known as...................................

Q3 Alpha radiation cannot penetrate far into the human body because it is stopped by our skin.

a) How can the insides of our body be affected by sources which emit alpha radiation?

....

b) What precautions should be taken by people handling alpha sources?

....

....

Q4 In industry, highly penetrating radiation sources sometimes need to be moved from place to place.

a) How can this be done without endangering the workers?

....

b) Gamma radiation can pass easily through the walls of buildings.
How can workers in the surrounding areas be protected from this hazard?

....

....

Risks from Radiation

Q5 Two scientists are handling their samples of radioactive material.

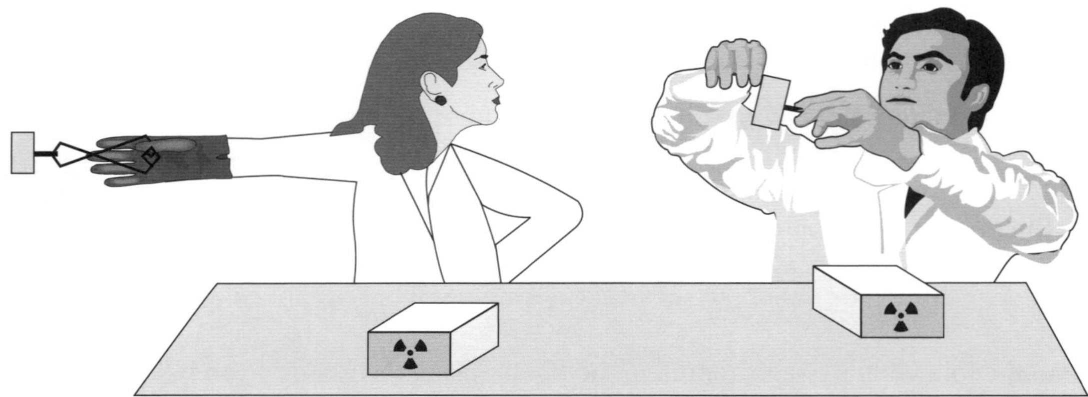

a) One of the scientists is taking sensible safety precautions, but the other is not. Describe three things which the careless scientist is doing wrong.

1. ....

2. ....

3. ....

b) Describe another way the scientists can reduce their exposure to the radiation when handling the samples, without using special apparatus or clothing.

....

c) How should radioactive samples be stored when they are not in use?

....

Q6 In 1986, a nuclear reactor at Chernobyl (in Ukraine) exploded, and a lot of radioactive material was released. Many people were exposed to very high doses of radiation. Since then, scientists have monitored the health of people living in the affected areas.

a) Why have scientists monitored people's health for so long after the explosion?

Think about half-life and dose.

....

....

b) The Chernobyl explosion provided scientists with new data about the effects of radiation exposure. Why could scientists not get this data by doing tests in a laboratory?

....

....

The Origin of the Universe

Q1 Scientists can tell how far away galaxies are by measuring the **red-shift** of the light coming from them.

a) How is **red-shifted** light from other galaxies **different** from the light we get from the Sun?

....

b) Explain how the red-shift changes as the galaxies become more distant from us.

....

c) What does this tell us about the speeds of nearer and more distant galaxies?

....

Q2 The sound of an ambulance siren changes as it approaches you and then moves away.

Circle A, B or C to show which of these statements is true.

A The frequency and the wavelength of the sound stay the same.

B The frequency gets lower as the ambulance approaches and higher as it moves away.

C The frequency gets higher as the ambulance approaches and lower as it moves away.

Q3 Brian set up a microphone at his local railway station to record his favourite **train noises**. He attached the microphone to an oscilloscope.

An express train passed through the station at a constant speed. Diagram A below shows the trace on the monitor at 11:31:07, as the train **approached** Brian's microphone.

On diagram B, sketch the trace Brian might have seen as the train **left** the station.

A

11:31:07

B

11:31:08

Q4 Complete this passage using the words supplied below.

expansion	matter	energy	expand	age	explosion

Many scientists believe that the Universe started with all the .... and .... in one small space. There was a huge .... and the material started to .... Scientists can estimate the .... of the Universe using the current rate of ....

Looking into Space

Q1 Earth-based telescopes and space telescopes have **different advantages**. Write the following advantages in the correct columns of the table.

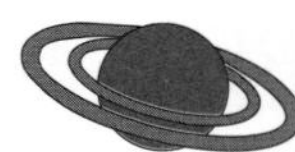

easier to install   easier to build   not vulnerable to pollution

cheaper   Earth's atmosphere doesn't get in the way

Earth-based telescopes	Space telescopes

Q2 Astronomers use various telescopes designed to collect different types of electromagnetic waves.

a) Why do they not just use **optical telescopes** situated on Earth or in space?

....

....

....

b) Astronomers can't use X-ray telescopes on Earth.
Explain why this is.

....

....

Top Tips: With telescopes, the rule is usually 'big is beautiful'. And it's best if you can think up a name to make sure everyone knows your telescope's the biggest. There's one in Chile called the Very Large Telescope. Imaginative. Better still, there are plans to build a really big new optical telescope — 100 m across — and call it the Overwhelmingly Large Telescope. Beat that.

Looking into Space

Q3 Only **one** of these statements about the Hubble Telescope is **true**.

Circle A, B, C or D to indicate which statement is correct.

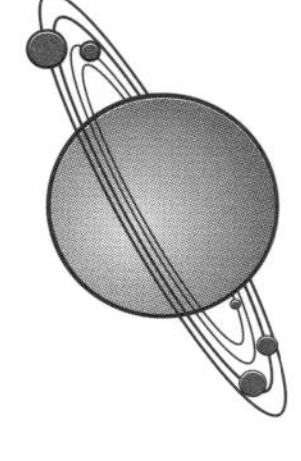

A It was placed in space in order to get closer to the stars.

B It is situated on a mountain top to get a clearer view into space.

C It uses radio waves rather than light waves to get a better picture of the stars.

D It was placed in space to avoid problems caused by the atmosphere.

Q4 Astronomers can use a number of strategies to improve the quality of the images they get of space.

a) How can they get good images of **faint**, **distant** objects using optical telescopes?

....

....

b) How can they improve an optical telescope's **resolution** (ability to see detail)?

....

....

Q5 Radio telescopes can see objects in space which cannot be seen by optical telescopes.

a) Describe **two other ways** in which radio telescopes are different from optical ones.

1. ....

2. ....

b) To produce images with a similar degree of detail, which would need to be **larger** — a radio telescope or an infrared telescope? Circle the correct answer.

radio infrared

Mixed Questions — Physics 1b

Q1 The waves A, B and C represent **infrared, visible light** and **ultraviolet** radiation (not in that order).

From A, B and C, write down in the boxes which wave:

a) has the shortest wavelength ☐

b) has the largest amplitude ☐

c) has the highest frequency ☐

d) represents ultraviolet radiation ☐

A

B

C

Q2 Radio Roary transmits **long-wave** signals with a wavelength of **1.5 km**.

a) Calculate the **frequency** of Radio Roary's transmission. (Use speed = 3×10^8 m/s.)

....

....

b) Mr Potts goes on holiday to the Scottish Highlands and stays in a cottage surrounded by mountains. While he's there, he follows England's progress in the cricket test match on Radio Roary.

Explain why Mr Potts gets **good** long-wave radio reception, even though he's surrounded by high mountains.

....

....

c) Another local radio station, Radio Piracy, broadcasts at a similar frequency to Radio Roary. Both stations broadcast analogue signals.

i) What problems might this cause for people listening to these stations?

....

....

ii) Suggest a way to avoid this problem, without changing the frequency of the transmissions.

....

Q3 In an **optical fibre**, light waves travel along an **inner core** made of glass or plastic.

Explain why the light waves don't 'escape' from this inner core, even though light normally passes through glass and plastic.

inner core

....

....

Mixed Questions — Physics 1b

Q4 Remote-sensing **satellites** can be used to 'see' the Earth from space. **Telescopes** can be put in space and used to 'see' other parts of the Universe.

a) Many satellites use microwaves to 'see' the Earth. These microwaves have a different wavelength from the microwaves used in ovens. Why is this important?

....

....

b) **i)** In what ways are space telescopes better than Earth-based ones?

....

ii) X-ray telescopes will **only** work from space. Why is this?

....

Q5 TV **remote controls** use infrared radiation. Jake shows Peter that he can change TV channels by pointing the remote control at a mirror on the opposite wall.

a) What property of EM rays has Jake demonstrated? Circle the correct answer.

reflection refraction diffraction

b) Peter places a dull black piece of card over the mirror and tries to change channel in the same way. It doesn't work. Explain why.

....

....

Q6 Cancer is sometimes treated using **gamma rays**.

a) When a substance **absorbs** any type of EM radiation, what two effects can occur?

....

b) When cells in the human body absorb a high dose of **gamma** rays, what happens to these cells?

....

c) Cancer can be **caused** by exposure to high frequency EM radiation — gamma, X-rays and UV rays.

i) Explain why high frequency radiation is generally more dangerous than low frequency radiation.

....

ii) Explain how X-rays can help doctors to diagnose fractured bones.

....

....

Mixed Questions — Physics 1b

Q7 The table gives information about four different **radioisotopes**.

Source	Type of Radiation	Half-life
radon-222	alpha	3.8 days
technetium-99m	gamma	6 hours
americium-241	alpha	432 years
cobalt-60	beta and gamma	5.27 years

a) Describe how the nucleus of a cobalt-60 atom is different from that of a 'normal' cobalt-59 atom.

....

b) Which source(s) in the table would be most suitable for using to detect leaks in pipes? Explain your answer.

....

....

c) Jim measures the count rate of a sample of technetium-99m as 160 cpm. Roughly how long would it take for the count rate to fall to **10 cpm**? Show your working.

....

....

Q8 The diagram represents a **light wave** emitted by a distant galaxy.

a) On the diagram, redraw the wave to show how it might appear to us on Earth because the light is **red-shifted**.

b) Explain how red-shifts from distant and nearer galaxies provide evidence for the Big Bang theory.

....

....

....

Q9 Why do astronomers often want to make telescopes as **big** as possible?

....

....

SAFW41